THE
AVICULTURIST'S
HANDBOOK

OTHER TITLES AVAILABLE
OR IN PRODUCTION

THE AVICULTURIST'S HANDBOOK

*The Management and Treatment of
Diseases, Disorders and Ailments*

by

LEON GOODMAN

NIMROD PRESS LTD
15 The Maltings
Turk Street
Alton, Hampshire, GU34 1DL
England

First Published, 1980
British and U.S.A. Edition, 1982
This Edition, 1989

ISBN: 1-85259-188-9

NIMROD PRESS LTD
15 The Maltings
Turk Street
Alton, Hampshire, GU34 1DL

Introduction

Those of us who get down in the dumps because of contemporary events might find an antidote in the history books. The trouble is that most of us had our school history given to us in doses about as palatable as cod liver oil; dates, names, battles, treaties, kings and rascals all strung together in a meaningless pattern one was expected to unravel.

Happy is the school boy or girl who has a teacher with enthusiasm and skill enough to make the subject come alive. Having done so he might make his mark on his pupils' thinking for life. But if on the other hand the teacher fails he could easily produce a generation of adults—be they artisans or scientists—who share the late lamented Henry Ford's celebrated but ignorant opinion that history is bunk.

My ambitious aim in this book is to emulate the teacher with enthusiasm and skill and to try to make the vast and interesting subject of birds' diseases, disorders and ailments, and the management thereof, come alive in a mere 100 pages. An impossible task you might say, but I believe that it can be done if the reader does not offend the basic principle of good medical diagnosis—namely to use one of God's greatest gifts to mankind, the ability to see and to observe. How often have you heard the lamented and all too familiar phrase—'my bird is dead—I gave it everything it needed but it just puffed up and died'? As a good doctor, your obvious question would be—'What were the symptoms and signs prior to its death?'

Needless to say the answer in most cases would be something like, 'I don't know, I did not see or observe anything unusual—maybe it was egg-bound, or it died of night fright; I don't know. What do you think it might have been?' These statements one could excuse were they coming from a novice breeder; but NOT from an 'old hand' who should be so trained in the observation of his birds that the slightest change in the birds' behaviour, appearance or condition would stand out like the proverbial 'sore thumb'.

When this is not the case, it simply illustrates that he is too lazy to use his eyes! Good medical diagnosis is based on OBSERVATION. Notice little things—be alert to the *first* signs of danger, for then the patient has a greater chance of recovery if treatment is commenced immediately.

Observe the symptoms. A bird cannot *tell* you what is wrong.

(a) Any undue listlessness.
(b) Lack of sheen on the plumage.
(c) Eyes lack lustre.
(d) Feathers look 'puffy'.
(e) Droppings are loose or a 'peculiar colour'.
(f) Appetite is abnormal or no appetite at all.
(g) Breathing is rapid, abdomen enlarged, etc.
(h) The ventral feathers are fouled.

And have you considered the bird's environment?

After considering all the facts one should now have a picture of the external symptoms of that particular disease, but remember these symptoms have a meaning only in relation to the changes taking place within the body and therefore they are simply indications of them.

Proper and correct treatment applied to the condition(s) for which it is intended is essential and can be done only through *correct diagnosis*.

Finches, waxbills and soft bills usually seem less prone to as many disorders as parrot-like birds and one should always look for the most common of these disorders, which are normally dietary and infectious in origin.

It is the aim of this book to take you through all the systems of the body, describing the normal anatomy and functions, for without knowing or understanding the NORMAL, you cannot expect to recognize the abnormal.

CHAPTER 1

Understanding Genetics

Basic genetics is not difficult to understand and yet so many of us 'shy away' from even trying to grasp the few simple fundamentals. It is on these basic fundamentals or foundations that you can, *with the aid of paper and pen*, build or break down your own breeding expectations and origins for any pair of breeding birds.

There are, however, certain facts you have to know about the birds you intend to breed or are using for breeding purposes. Here I would dare to say that *feather colour* is the main object or concern of most breeders and this aspect has been adequately dealt with in books appertaining to the particular species.

This chapter has been written to clarify certain facts and misconceptions which have not been dealt with adequately in other books—too much has been 'assumed' of the reader's knowledge of genetics!

Remember, to understand genetics, use a pen and paper as you would when confronted with an arithmetical problem. Here goes:

All forms of life are made up of cells. From the simple unicellular organisms to man, each cell has its own identity. In birds, like man, the body comprises groups of cells forming *tissues* and the tissues in turn are grouped together to form *organs*. Organs are grouped to form SYSTEMS.

To understand *genetics*, which can be defined as the UNITS of INHERITANCE, we must return to the *single cell*, from which all forms of life begin.

In the heart or nucleus of each and every cell there are, besides other structures, minute rod-like structures or chains of genes called chromosomes (colour bodies). These chromosomes always occur in pairs, and the number of pairs of chromosomes is *always* the same for members of the *same species*, i.e. man has 23 pairs and rabbits have 22 pairs.

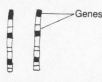

1 pair.chromosornes

Each gene occupies a particular place, or locus, in the chain. Since the chromosomes occur in pairs, *the genes also occur in pairs*. Of the 23 pairs of chromosomes in man, *22 pairs* are alike (homologous) while *one pair* is unlike and is termed the *sex chromosomes* or X and Y chromosomes. (They are shaped like an X and Y—see later.)

In birds, like man, propagation of the species occurs by sexual reproduction, i.e. fusion of the male sperm cell with that of the female egg cell or ovum. Now you might well ask: 'Why, if two cells each containing *23 pairs* of chromosomes fuse, surely you end up with one large cell containing *46 pairs* of chromosomes?' Fortunately this does not happen because by a unique process of reduced cell division (meiosis) of chromosomes in the SEX CELLS (sperm and ovum), there are only *half* the number of chromosomes in each, i.e. 23 *un*paired chromosomes. Therefore, when fusion of the sex cells occurs only *half* the genetic material from one parent is 'mixed' with *half* that of the other parent and consequently the original number of chromosomes or 23 pairs is restored.

The fusion or mixing of the chromosomes—and hence genes—results in various and vast genetic combinations affecting such factors as colour of the skin, eyes, hair texture, etc.

To complicate matters still further a particular gene, say from the male ($\male$), will dominate the gene from the female ($\female$) or vice versa and is called a DOMINANT GENE, while the other is called a RECESSIVE GENE. These dominant and recessive genes are specific for a particular trait, e.g. the gene for brown eyes is dominant to the gene for blue eyes. It can also happen that *both* genes are dominant or recessive (homozygous genes) or that there is an incomplete dominance (heterozygous) (1 dominant and 1 recessive) or even an absence thereof, as seen when a red cow is mated with a white bull and the offspring is neither red nor white but a roan colour. Recessive genes (weak traits) can linger from generation to generation without being revealed. This condition is occasionally seen in man in the form of dwarfs, albinos, deafmutes etc., when there is a 'chance' meeting of *two recessive genes*. Normally in man these harmful defects are 'bred out' but some people may remain 'carriers' of the recessive trait.

Fortunately, in most cases one gene is normally dominant although sometimes incomplete.

1st Example (Mendel's Law of Segregation)

N—denotes a normal DOMINANT GENE OR TRAIT
n—denotes an abnormal RECESSIVE GENE OR TRAIT

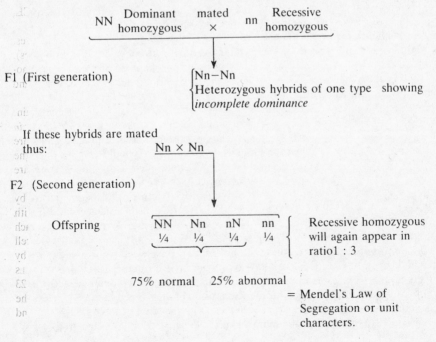

2nd Example (Mendel's Law of Incomplete Dominance)

W−Dominant White gene   Neither colour is dominant
B−Dominant Black gene   over the other.

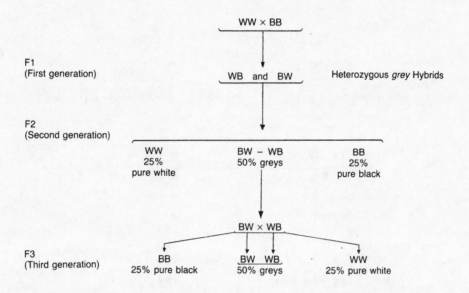

WW × BB

F1
(First generation)

WB   and   BW   Heterozygous *grey* Hybrids

F2
(Second generation)

WW	BW − WB	BB
25%	50% greys	25%
pure white		pure black

BW × WB

F3
(Third generation)

BB	BW WB	WW
25% pure black	50% greys	25% pure white

INDEFINITE RATIO OF 1 : 3

3

3rd Example (Mendel's Law of Independent Assortment)

Here it will be shown how the characters or traits segregate and recombine independently in each generation, in the crossing of hybrids, the dominant and recessive characters being inherited in *definite* ratios.

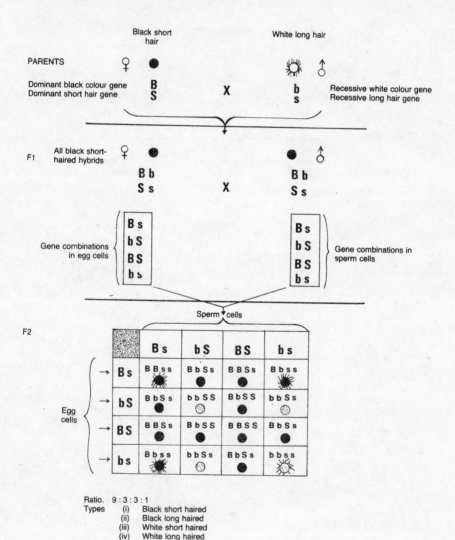

Ratio. 9 : 3 : 3 : 1
Types   (i)   Black short haired
        (ii) Black long haired
        (iii) White short haired
        (iv) White long haired

SEX CHROMOSOMES

As stated before, *every cell* in the *human body* has 23 pairs of chromosomes of which the 22 pairs are *homologous* chromosomes (collectively known as autosomes) while the remaining pair are called the *sex chromosomes* or X and Y chromosomes. Although most genetic traits are carried by the 22 pairs of autosomes, there are certain traits, besides sex determination, that are carried by the genes of the X–Y chromosomes. (See later.) They are called X–Y because the chromosomes are similarly shaped. Let us first observe how these X and Y chromosomes determine the sex of the offspring.

The male (♂) cell contains an X and Y chromosome while the female (♀) cell contains an X and X chromosome. It is the way in which these sex cells combine that determines the sex of the offspring.

Note: **In birds and moths the situation is reversed, i.e. the female (♀) ovum carries the X–Y chromosomes while the male (♂) sperm carries the X–X chromosomes. Therefore *only* in these *two* species of animal does the female determine the sex of the offspring. It is an unusual 'evolutionary' condition which exists for which no explanation can be found!**

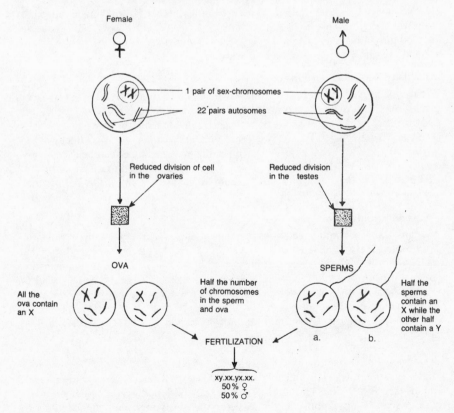

If an ovum is fertilized by an X-carrying sperm (a) the union gives rise to an *XX* combination or FEMALE and when fertilized by a Y-carrying sperm (b) it gives rise to an *XY* combination or MALE. (See diagram page 5.)

Thus sex is determined at the time of conception. It is determined by the sex chromosomes in the parental sex cells and, in *most* animals, it is determined by the MALE. In birds, however, it is determined by the FEMALE.

SEX FACTORS IN GENES

1. Sex-linked Genes

Many characteristics are associated with the sexes, but some are directly determined by the genes that are carried on the sex chromosomes, particularly on the X chromosomes. For the genes are carried on and transmitted through the X chromosomes; these genes are referred to as *sex-linked*. Note: The Y chromosome does carry some genes, although it does not contain any of the sex-linked genes referred to above, but merely carries the *sex-characteristics* of the *male* species.

Some examples of sex-linked genes:

(i) The normal feather colour of the Gouldian Finch is sex-linked but the *white-breast colour only* is not sex-linked.

(ii) Colour blindness and haemophilia in man are due to recessive sex-linked genes and are more common in men than women.

2. Partially Sex-linked Genes

There is a part of the X chromosome which is homologous with the Y chromosome, and certain genes are carried on the homologous parts of both X and Y. Crossing over can occur between such genes. In a female, the crossing over will merely move the genes from one X chromosome to the other, and the effect will be the ordinary one of exchanging genes. But in the male the genes will be exchanged from X to Y or from Y to X, and will therefore be transmitted to offspring of the sex opposite to that to which they would have been transmitted before the exchange.

3. Sex-influenced Genes

Sometimes the dominant relations of a pair of alleles (corresponding sites of two chromosomes) are reversed in the two sexes. For example, in sheep a factor H results in horns while its allele h results in no horns. However, H is dominant in males, while h is dominant in females. Hence animals of the genotype HH will be horned, those of hh will be hornless. Males of the genotype Hh will be horned, while females of this genotype will be hornless. In man, baldness, one form of white forelock (Charlie Weir) and absence of certain teeth are inherited in this way.

LETHAL GENES

These are genes which produce fatal effects. They have been found in plants and animals (see BALDNESS, Chapter 7). A sex-linked lethal gene markedly affects the sex ratio among the offspring: males carrying this type of gene do not survive.

Sickle-cell anaemia is caused by a lethal gene. X-rays can cause lethal genes to be formed (see also mutations).

MUTATION OF GENES

The theory of gene mutation was first formulated by Hugo de Vries in 1900.

Each gene occupies a definite spot, or locus, in a chromosome. These loci or spots are usually named for the effect of the gene occupying that locus. At one locus on one of the human chromosomes, for example, there is a gene which results in normal pigmentation of skin, eyes and hair. As long as every gene at this locus resulted in normal pigmentation, we could not know of the existence of this locus, since all persons would be alike in this character.

But genes occasionally undergo changes in their composition, known as MUTA-TIONS. The changed or mutant gene results in a new and different trait, and after the change a dominant mutant gene reproduces its new form just as faithfully as it formerly reproduced its previous form. An albino or albinism is an example where the mutant gene fails to produce one of the enzymes to form the pigment melanin.

Many thousands of mutant genes are known. Frequently the mutant gene is recessive to its normal allele; occasionally one is dominant or sometimes neither.

While some mutant genes produce harmless effects, such as changes in the hair colour, most of them result in detrimental effects (see lethal genes).

Man has the power to select consciously mutations that suit his fancy and he is able to combine these mutations into new arrangements. In this way many breeds and varieties can be established or developed.

Causes of Mutations

(1) Occur normally by chemical rearrangement or changes in the gene mole-cule.
(2) Drastic environmental factors such as X-rays, radium rays, ultra-violet light, and certain chemicals such as mustard gas.

CHAPTER 2

The Digestive Tract and Related Organs

THE COMPONENTS AND FUNCTIONS OF THE DIGESTIVE TRACT
(Refer to diagrams overleaf) (Pages 9 & 10).

Beak, mouth and tongue   Responsible for ingestion of food (Pages 9 & 10).

Gullet   Passageway to crop.

Crop   Ingested food accumulates here and is slowly 'fed' to the proventriculus (see crop impaction).

Proventriculus   A true-glandular stomach.

Gizzard   Strong muscular organ, contains small stones, which by movements of the muscles grind the food (seed) to a pulp. A valve at its exit allows 'pulp' to pass into the duodenum. Obstruction by seed hulls, in young birds, can occur in gizzard. The above organs are not normally prone to disorders, except tumours (growths).

Intestine

    (i) Duodenum—forms a long loop in which lies the pancreas. Bile and pancreatic ducts open into the duodenum. Refer to pages 10 and 11 for function.

    (ii) Jejunum and ileum—make up most of the intestines. The intestine terminates in the rectum.

Terminal Part

    (i) Rectum—plays a small part in digestion.

    (ii) Cloaca—expanded portion at end of rectum which serves as the common antrum (chamber) for the ureters and sexual ducts.

    (iii) Vent—external orifice through which pass waste products of digestion; it is also the reproductive aperture (opening).

ASSOCIATED AND RELATED ORGANS

1. Liver
2. Pancreas
3. Spleen

1. **Liver**

The largest organ in the body.

(i) Produces bile which is stored in the gall-bladder and from there passes into the duodenum when required for digestion of fats (pigeons and doves have *no* gall-bladder).

(ii) Responsible for formation and destruction of red blood cells.

(iii) Detoxifies poisons and chemicals.

(iv) Stores vitamins.

N.B. If a bird does not eat, bile accumulates in the gall-bladder until it becomes distended; bile will then flow into the duodenum, staining the empty intestine *green*.

DIGESTIVE TRACT COMPONENTS

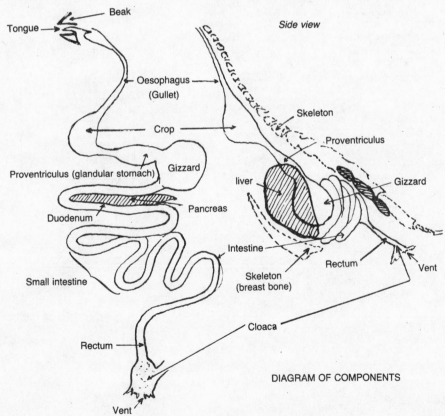

DIAGRAM OF COMPONENTS

DIAGRAMMATICAL PRESENTATION OF THE
FUNCTIONS OF DIGESTIVE TRACT AND RELATED ORGANS

CHART 1

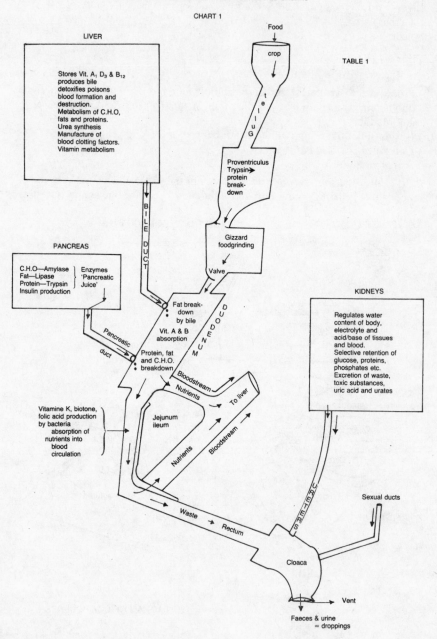

TABLE 1

LIVER

Stores Vit. A, D₃ & B₁₂
produces bile
detoxifies poisons
blood formation and
destruction.
Metabolism of C.H.O,
fats and proteins.
Urea synthesis
Manufacture of
blood clotting factors.
Vitamin metabolism

Food

crop

Gullet

Proventriculus
Trypsin → protein break-down

Gizzard
foodgrinding

Valve

PANCREAS

C.H.O—Amylase
Fat—Lipase
Protein—Trypsin
Insulin production

Enzymes
'Pancreatic
Juice'

BILE DUCT

Pancreatic duct

Fat break-down by bile

Vit. A & B absorption

Protein, fat and C.H.O. breakdown

DUODENUM

Bloodstream

Nutrients

To liver

KIDNEYS

Regulates water
content of body,
electrolyte and
acid/base of tissues
and blood.
Selective retention of
glucose, proteins,
phosphates etc.
Excretion of waste,
toxic substances,
uric acid and urates

Vitamine K, biotone,
folic acid production
by bacteria
absorption of
nutrients into
blood
circulation

Jejunum
ileum

Nutrients

Bloodstream

URETERS

Sexual ducts

Waste → Rectum

Cloaca

Vent

Faeces & urine
= droppings

Lesions of the Liver

Involved in most diseases and ailments and the most frequently seen are:

(i) alimentary hepatitis due to excess fat, where the liver is enlarged, and discoloured (yellow or whitish liver);

Hepatitis. Enlarged liver—visible through abdominal wall

(ii) haemorrhagic (darkish red areas) lesions of variable size may be seen in some poisonings and streptococcal infections (see Infections);

(iii) soft yellow or whitish spots as seen in typhoid, pseudotuberculosis, tuberculosis and diphtheria;

(iv) tumours or growths are also found;

(v) rupture of the liver—causes sudden death and is seen in
   (a) several infectious diseases,
   (b) obese birds,
   (c) injury.

2. The Pancreas

Two Functions

Digestive and hormonal, i.e. it produces diastase enzyme (see page 10) and the hormone insulin which regulates the blood sugar.

Disorders of the pancreas are infrequent.

3. The Spleen

Functions

Iron and blood storage. Destruction and manufacture of blood cells.

Disorders

In most instances it is indirectly involved in generalized disorders.

CHAPTER 3

Nutrition and Metabolism and Associated Disorders

All birds are made alike.
They are made of bones, flesh and food.
Only the foods are different.

Most of our efforts, time and money are devoted to 'feeding' our birds. Utilize these precious commodities intelligently and you will be rewarded. I have seen, and been guilty of it myself, that one's first reaction, when one is confronted with a bird that's 'all puffed up', is to run to the medicine cupboard (some are virtual chemist shops), take the poor bird and pump it full of some 'cure-all' only to discover the next day that it has departed this life.

95% of our losses are attributed directly or indirectly to nutritional disorders. Isn't it so in human beings?

Remember, there are only THREE MAIN CAUSES of nutritional disorders:

A. NOT ENOUGH FOOD.

B. WRONG FOOD.

C. TOO MUCH FOOD (OVERFEEDING).

Before elaborating on these, let us see what constitutes a balanced diet and what nutrition is all about; for if you know that your birds are receiving a 'balanced diet', are hopefully not handicapped physically and anatomically, then you are already 95% on the way to success.

A balanced diet for most seed eaters should comprise the following (refer to charts below and on pages 13 and 14):

(a) Carbohydrates

(b) Fats

(c) Protein

(d) Vitamins

(e) Minerals and trace elements

(f) Grit and fibre and an adequate supply of *fresh* water.

CARBOHYDRATES, FATS AND PROTEINS
(95% of Food Requirements)

Food	Source	Function	Deficiencies or excess
1. CARBOHYDRATES (C.H.O.) (i) Starches (ii) Sugars (iii) Cellulose	Vegetable foods Egg Yolk Milk Liver Canary Millets (very rich)	Energy Food. Can be converted to fats. *N.B.* A bird will stop eating once its energy needs are fulfilled even if its other needs are not.	Deficiencies are very rare in healthy birds. C.H.O. can be made from fat in the body, liver and gastro-intestinal tract. Dysfunction can lead to deficiencies of all food. (See Cycles page 19.)

12

Food	Source	Function	Deficiencies or excess
2. FATS Fatty acids and glycerine	Vegetable oils animal fats rape, maw and niger C.L.O.* egg yolk	Maintain body temperature. Excess are stored in tissues and *liver*. Requirement increases in cold weather. *N.B.* Beware of rancid fats (i.e. fats exposed to heat and air)	Excess fat causes obesity etc. See Lesions of the Liver, page 9
3. PROTEINS (± 20% of food intake required)	Seed and grain germs, rape, maw, soya etc. Practically all animal products.	Tissue builder → Growth (Provides nitrogen)	Deficiency leads to death

* C.L.O. = Cod Liver Oil

VITAMINS

	Vitamin sources	Function	Deficiency
Fat Soluble	A C.L.O. Egg Yolk Greens and Fruits	Growth Skin Eye (visual purple formation) Stored in liver	Poor vision Thyroid, ovary and respiratory dysfunction
	D3 Action of sunlight on fatty tissue Sunflower Seeds C.L.O. Egg Yolk	Anti-rachitic (Rickets) Corrects Ca-P. balance	Rickets, nervous disorders Excess leads to calcium deposits in kidneys, blood vessels
	E Fresh Greens Seed Germs Egg Yolk Wheat Germ Oil	Fertility vitamin	Infertility
	K Greens and Fruit Intestinal bacterial synthesis (made in gut)	Blood clotting	Haemorrhage
Water Soluble	B1 Brewer's Yeast Seed Germs and Oils B2 ⎫ Animal products B3 ⎬ Vegetables B5 ⎭ Molasses B6	Essential for growth, health, all body functions	Very rare
	B12 Animal products i.e. egg yolk and milk	Fat and C.H.O. metabolism, Neural function, Maturation of red blood cells	Rare
	C Not required by birds: made by the body.		

To ensure adequate requirements, it is best to supply synthetic vitamin preparations to the birds' diet (see Chemotherapy and Drugs), e.g. Abidec—2
drops/50 cc of water, twice a week.

MINERALS AND TRACE ELEMENTS

(2–5% of Needs)

(A) MINERALS—Necessary in large quantities

Mineral	Source	Function	Deficiency
Ca In the form of Calcium phosphate Calcium carbonate	All foodstuffs and water Bone, Egg Shell, Oyster Shell and Cuttlefish. Supplied as dicalcium phosphate	Acid/base balance Bone/egg formation Blood clotting Enzyme production Nerve tissue C.H.O. and fat Metabolism	Decreases Vit D3 → ↓ Bone formation → Rickets and also soft egg shells
Mg Magnesium sulphate	Plants (Greens) & Cuttlefish, Bone etc.	Bone formation C.H.O. metabolism	As for Ca
P Phosphates (mineral phosphorus)	As for calcium	As for Ca	
Na and Cl K and I Sodium chloride Potassium iodide Sodium iodide	Common salt* All foods and Rocksalt. Cuttlefish Bone meal	Fluid balance Growth, fertility Protein metabolism Reproduction and life	Feather plucking Infertility Thyroid malfunction Loss of weight

(B) TRACE ELEMENTS—Necessary in small quantities and present in most foodstuffs and H_2O occur in chemical combination with other elements.

Mn Manganese	Grains/greens	Bone formation
Fe Iron	H_2O	Blood formation
Cu Copper		Blood formation
Zn Zinc		Enzyme production
Co Cobalt		Feathers and vit. B12
Se Selenium		
Br Bromine		
S Sulphur		

* NaCl—Must be supplied as an extra supplement to the diet—*do not add to the water or food, bird will consume salt according to its needs.*

Grit (River Bed Silica) must always be available. It is not a trace element and is not digested. It acts as an AID to digestion.

It is not in the scope of this book to present you with 'diet sheets' for all the different birds. The requirements of the Australian Grass Finches (my own favourite) have been selected.

(i) Standard seed mixture made up of equal parts canary and millets. To this is added small quantities of niger, manna and maw, and when available a separate container of wild grass seeds.

(ii) Well-washed freshly sprouted seeds or millet spray (soak seeds or sprays for 24 hours and leave to drain for ± 3 days in a warm room) should always be available to the birds. Note: *Soaked seed* is seed that is soaked for 24 hours, washed and given to birds immediately, as compared to sprouted seed. Both forms are beneficial and readily taken by the birds.

(iii) Just before and during breeding season, a fresh mixture (made up daily) of Lopis Canary Rearing and Conditioning Food to which is added, in equal proportions, freshly hard-boiled (20 minutes) egg yolk. To this can be added, if desired, some form of live food such as chopped-up mealworms or termites. Optional—5 ml *purified* babies' cod liver oil (C.L.O.) added to 0,5 kg dry seed mixture and allowed to stand for 24 hours may be fed during the winter period. Only enough seed, which can normally be consumed in *one* day should be treated (see RANCID FATS). Any seed that is not eaten should be thoroughly washed and used for the soaked seed mixture.

Note: Sunflower oil is preferable as it does not go rancid!

(iv) Fresh greens—well-washed (see Poisons), must be available every day of the year—e.g. Chickweed, winter grass, dandelion, lettuce (green parts), groundsel, watercress, finely sliced spinach and most important, if available, unripened seeding—grass heads.

(v) Finally—in separate containers—insoluble and soluble branded tonic grits—finely flaked cuttlefish-bone (100% $CaCO_3$)—well-baked egg-shell—coarse salt or rocksalt—charcoal lumps and, last but not least, grit. Fine river-bed grit or silica (insoluble and essential for digestion) has *rounded* edges (does not irritate) and should pass through a 16-mesh screen. Don't forget a fresh (changed daily) supply of water.

Note: ± 70% of the tissues of most higher animals consist of water.

GUIDE TO SPECIALIZED DIETS

Soft food supplement suitable for breeding birds as follows, e.g. hard bills, wax bills and canaries etc.

Dried bread crumbs	14 parts
Dried skimmed milk	2 parts
Bran	1 part
Wheat germ (not oil)	1 part
Peanut oil	1 part
Sunflower oil	1 part
Iodized salt	1 part
Dried egg yolk	1 part
	22 parts

Substitutes for Insectile or Live Foods are as follows:

(a)	Fine biscuit meal	7 parts
	Dried whole milk powder	1 part
	Wheat germ (not oil)	1 part
	White fish meal	1 part
		10 parts

15

(b)	Fine biscuit or baby rusk.........	2 parts
	Shrimp meal or dried flies........	1 part
	Dried egg yolk	1 part
	Honey	1 part
	Wheat germ (not oil)...........	1 part
	Sunflower oil	1 part
		7 parts

MAIN CAUSES OF NUTRITIONAL AND DIGESTIVE DISORDERS

It is important to recall that digestive disorders are associated with most diseases which occur in acute and chronic forms. *It is only* in their chronic forms that these disorders could be confused with purely digestive disorders.

A. NOT ENOUGH FOOD

This is either due *directly* to *quantitative* underfeeding—leading to frank starvation

OR

indirectly, due to some disorder or disease process such as:

1. **Defective Intake**

    (a) Congenital or acquired malformation of the beak, eyes, tongue etc.—the bird is unable to eat.

    (b) Mechanical obstruction of the upper or lower digestive tract as may be caused by worms, tumours and seed hulls etc. (see Crop Impaction).

    (c) Loss of appetite—due to fevers (see Diseases).

2. **Defective Digestion and Absorption**

    (a) Prolonged antibiotic therapy.

    (b) Worms and coccidiosis (see Diseases).

3. **Defective Utilization**

    As in liver disease.

4. **Loss of Nutrients from the Body**

    (a) Kidney disease.

    (b) Haemorrhage.

    (c) Diarrhoea.

5. **Increased Nutritional Needs**

    Periods of stress such as breeding, moulting and cold weather (see Wrong Food).

B. WRONG FOOD

Directly due to a *qualitative* dietary deficiency resulting in malnutrition.

(a) Stale, mouldy or rancid food.

(b) Lack of specific nutrient, e.g. rickets, sterility, retarded growth, etc.

(c) Unsuitable size gravel.

(d) Lack of greens.

(e) Failure to vary diet according to the birds' needs, e.g. breeding season, moulting, etc.

(f) Unsuitable diet for the species of bird, e.g. feeding only dried seeds leads to increased uric acid and also constipation. (See Chart page 19.)

C. TOO MUCH FOOD

(a) Overfeeding, especially high-fat diet (see Liver).

(b) Lack of exercise.

COMMON SYMPTOMS OF DIGESTIVE DISORDERS

1. Enlarged and inflamed abdomen—usually intestines are visible.
2. Appetite *appears* to be normal (but, if closely observed, bird spits out most seed) or excessive (seed passes right through the digestive tract and is seen as such in the faeces).
3. Bird may scatter its seed (see Wrong Food).
4. Increased thirst.
5. Droppings—vary from dry to thin, watery, soft and yellow.

Differential Diagnosis (see Diseases)

Avian diphtheria, coccidiosis, B. paratyphoid, worms, nephritis, vit. B deficiency or respiratory disease.

SOME COMMON SYMPTOMS AND MISCONCEPTIONS

1. Droppings or Excreta

(a) Colour and consistency may merely indicate that the bird has been eating some particular food, but may be important indications as to the state of its health. Considered in conjunction with other facts, they may be the deciding factor between an incorrect and a correct diagnosis.

'Normal droppings' are white (urine) and black (faeces).

The colour of the faeces can be influenced by the food, but there are few foods that have any influence upon the colour of the urine. There are exceptions. Observation of these changes is important so that when a disease gets into your flock you will be prepared.

(b) *Constipation.* Usually caused by a plain seed diet.

Signs: Droppings are firm and dry.

Difficulty in forcing a passage, cf. diarrhoea.

(c) Diarrhoea—Excess water in the faeces. Diarrhoea is a *symptom of a particular* disease/disorder, which may arise either in the digestive tract, circulatory, genito-urinary or respiratory systems.

Any inflammation of the gut lining membranes or cloacal lining membranes causes increased secretion of fluid (mucus), and droppings become soft, viscid, pasty or watery. Because of the acidic nature of the secretions, they in turn further irritate the delicate lining of the cloaca and vent. This causes pain and the bird will 'whip' its tail after each passage.

During the interval between motions, the highly inflamed walls of the vent tend to stick together. This in turn may cause the bird to strain in order to force the next passage (cf constipation).

As mentioned previously, diarrhoea can be due only to an excess of water intake by the bird, e.g. fruit, drinking-water too rich in minerals or too much greens. *Never* reduce or remove drinking-water, but correct the cause.

Nestling Diarrhoea—See Diseases.

Green Diarrhoea—due to the presence of bile pigments. Also present if bird does not eat at all (see Liver Function).

White Diarrhoea. Due to excess urate in faeces. See also Kidney Disease.

(d) Enteritis. (Inflammation of the intestinal lining.) Enteritis must not be confused with diarrhoea, which may be present without enteritis. Often they occur together.

2. Crop Impaction

Signs and symptoms. Crop enlarged and bird in distress. Common in young birds—caused by seed hulls, etc. that will not pass through the crop. Pressure on the trachea leads to suffocation. This condition is usually fatal and must not be confused with sour crop.

3. Sour Crop

Causes—usually dietary or infectious (see First Aid).

4. Puffed Abdomen

This is a symptom of a disease or disorder. The abdomen is the most important part of the bird's anatomy which can *aid* diagnosis. But just as a man's pulse does not diagnose the condition it will tell the doctor what is *not* wrong with the patient. Therefore if we examine the bird's abdomen and can *see* the liver and intestines we can tentatively diagnose either typhoid, or Avian diphtheria, or coccidiosis etc. If, however, these organs are *not* visible then surely we can exclude those diseases!

CHART 2

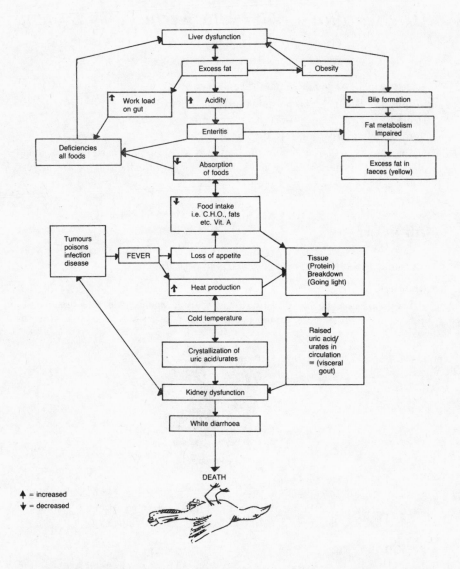

♠ = increased
♥ = decreased

With a little intelligent imagination the effects of various diseases, disorders etc. can be followed on the cycle, and conclusions reached.

CHAPTER 4

The Cardiovascular and Respiratory Systems

(The heart, blood and blood vessels, and lungs)

Some Normal Physiological Data (See also page xi)

Respiratory Rate   ± 90 per minute (Man 16 p.m.)
Heart Rate   ± 300–500 beats per minute (Man 70 p.m.)
Body Temperature   ± 40°–44°C (Man is 37°C)

The blood vascular system of the bird is like that of mammals, being formed by blood vessels (arteries, veins and capillaries) through which the heart circulates (pumps) blood.

THE CARDIOVASCULAR SYSTEM

THE HEART

Situated in the chest cavity, the heart is a chambered, muscular pump. It is surrounded by a protective membrane, the pericardium.

Disorders

The heart may be invaded by disease-causing agents (see Infections) and an inflammation of the pericardium (pericarditis) is often observed. In such cases a

Pericarditis

purulent (pus-like) and cloudy liquid may be found in variable quantity, between the pericardium and the heart. This liquid may sometimes form a solid, fibrinous material and the heart appears to be surrounded by a whitish envelope.

BLOOD VESSELS

Caged birds live comparatively longer than their natural counterparts and may therefore be more prone to vascular disorders. Arteriosclerosis (hardening of the arteries) occurs in 'old birds' and the symptoms may not be distinct—the bird may suddenly die of a ruptured artery or have leg problems due to a slowing down or even obstruction of the circulation to the legs (see Legs).

20

Blood Disorders

Cases of these have been reported but are not common, e.g. leucoses (similar to leukaemia) and anaemia. Anaemia is probably the most common disorder and is due to a lack of or decreased number of red blood cells in the circulation.

Symptoms

   (i) Pale skin and mucosa
  (ii) Weakness and lethargy

Causes

    (i) Age
   (ii) In-breeding
  (iii) Infectious or parasitic diseases
  (iv) Poisoning or deficiencies (see Diet)
   (v) Digestive ailments (hepatitis)
  (vi) Presence of red mites
 (vii) Internal or external haemorrhage

Treatment

Based on correct diagnosis and removal of cause (if known). Feed bird on a rich varied ration of vit. B12, minerals and iron salts.

HAEMORRHAGES (Bleeding)

Some causes are:

    (i) Fragility of blood vessels (not common)
   (ii) Shock (meningeal haemorrhage)
  (iii) Vit. K deficiency (rare)
  (iv) Some toxins, e.g. aspergillosis
   (v) Infectious diseases (pox virus)
  (vi) Rupturing of an organ due to some lesion
 (vii) Direct injury

Although the aforementioned disorders do occur they are mainly of academic interest and from a practical standpoint very little can normally be done in most of these cases. The respiratory system, however, is very prone to diseases, disorders and ailments and will be discussed in more detail.

THE RESPIRATORY SYSTEM

The respiratory system's main functions are the oxygenation of the blood, elimination of carbon dioxide (CO_2) and water evaporation; the latter plays a major role in the regulation of the bird's body temperature.

For descriptive purposes the respiratory tract is divided into an upper and a lower respiratory tract, the dividing line being the lower border of the syrinx or voice (song) box located at the lower end of the trachea (windpipe). This division is an artificial one and *must not* be allowed to obscure the intimate relationship between upper and lower respiratory disease.

21

1. The Upper Respiratory Tract

This comprises—
A—nostrils, B—nasal fossae, C—nasopharynx, D—nasal sinuses. E—trachea or windpipe and F—syrinx

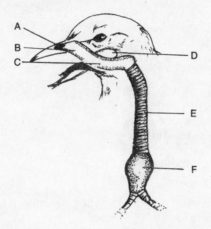

The nostrils communicate with the sinuses, located under the eyes and forward, toward the beak. The trachea is a cylindrical and rigid tube, transparent and ringed. At its end is the syrinx, consisting of a vibrant membrane sustained by a central bone. After the syrinx, the trachea divides (see lower respiratory tract) into two bronchi, leading to the lungs (see later).

As the respiratory tract is *one system*, the disorders relating to the upper tract will be discussed together with the lower tract.

2. The Lower Respiratory System

Comprises the bronchi, bronchioles, alveoli (air sacs) and pleural membranes which form a protective covering for the lungs. Normal lung tissue is pale pink, of

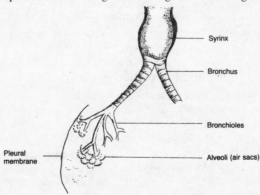

porous structure and will float in water. The lungs are situated in the chest cavity and lie against the backbone on either side.

In addition to the lungs, a large number of respiratory auxiliaries or air sacs are widely distributed throughout the body in the principal bones, and a complex system of interconnecting tubes which carry air from the lungs and bronchi to almost all parts of the body structure, including the quills of the feathers.

There are four main pairs of air sacs, delineated by thin transparent membranes; filled with air they make the bird lighter and flying easier (see diagram below). These air sacs are difficult to see in small birds.

RESPIRATORY TRACT
Lungs (L) and Air Sacs (AS)

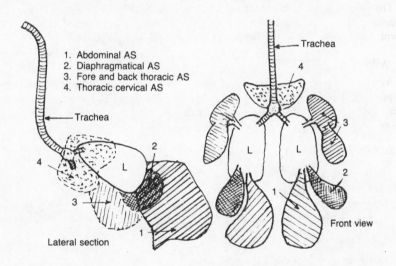

1. Abdominal AS
2. Diaphragmatical AS
3. Fore and back thoracic AS
4. Thoracic cervical AS

Trachea

Trachea

Lateral section

Front view

SOME COMMON DISORDERS AFFECTING THE RESPIRATORY SYSTEM

Please refer to Chapter 9 in this book for more detailed description of the *diseases*.

1. Sinusitis—Rhinitis—Common Cold or Coryza
2. Bronchitis and Tracheitis
3. Asthma
4. Pneumonia and other infections (see Chapter 9)
5. Air Sacculitis
6. Subcutaneous Emphysema

1. Sinusitis—Rhinitis—Coryza or the Common Cold

Symptoms

Sneezing, coughing, nasal discharge and watery eyes.

Causes

(a) It may be mild; induced by cold or due to local bacterial or viral infection.

(b) It may be more severe and associated with contagious respiratory disease.

(c) It may be due to vit. A deficiency.

(d) Sinusitis may be complicated, resulting in sub-orbital swelling (blepharitis) with pus formation, which must be removed by puncture with syringe and needle and filling the cavity with an antibiotic solution. Vitamins must be given in all cases. (See First Aid.) *If not controlled, a minor infection of the upper tract can spread to involve the entire respiratory system.*

2. Bronchitis and Tracheitis

The viral disease called Infectious Bronchitis is specific to poultry; other bird species are not affected. As stated before, the bronchi and trachea are commonly involved in disorders of the other parts of the respiratory system.

3. Asthma

Asthma, as a specific disease in birds, *does not exist.* What we observe are *respiratory symptoms* of gasping, wheezing or rapid, noisy and whistling respiration due to the presence of mucus in the trachea, i.e. 'Asthma' in birds is a symptom of many unrelated conditions or disorders.

Some common causes

Long-term Disease (refer to Chapter 9):
(a) Infectious respiratory disease

(b) Acariasis (lung mite)

(c) Nutritional (dietary)

(d) Gape worm

Short-term Disease with Death:
(a) Aspergillosis

(b) Pox

(c) Avian diphtheria.

4. Pneumonia and Other Infections

Pneumonia; or more correctly pneumonitis, is not a common occurrence in cage birds and is often a misdiagnosed case of nephritis (inflammation of one or both kidneys).

Symptoms

Usually a sudden onset—bird is 'puffed up' and sleeps most of the time. Droppings during the early stages are brown with little or no urine; later there are *no* droppings with death ensuing reasonably soon.

Treatment: Tetracyclines or sulphadimidine (Sulphamezathine—see Chapter 11).

For other infectious and contagious diseases and disorders see Chapter 9.

24

5. Air Sacculitis

An infection of the air sacs by a variety of 'germs', chiefly colibaccilli, is frequent in respiratory disease and on post-mortem findings the air sacs contain a pale yellow pus.

6. Subcutaneous Emphysema

A rare and individual condition. The bird is 'swollen' due to the presence of *air* under the skin, which may arise from any part of the respiratory tract, often following damage to an air sac.

Treatment: Puncturing the swollen skin to allow air to escape; relapses are common and the procedure is to be repeated until permanent recovery takes place.

CHAPTER 5

Urogenital System

(Kidneys and Reproductive Systems)

These two systems are closely linked anatomically but are described separately in this chapter.

KIDNEYS

These are made up of three lobes of unequal size and lie along each side of the lumbar (lower back) spine and fill the hollow of the pelvic bones. They are connected with the cloaca by the ureters. See diagram below. In birds, the urine is not liquid but pasty in consistency. It contains the end products (mainly) of protein metabolism, i.e. urates and uric acid.

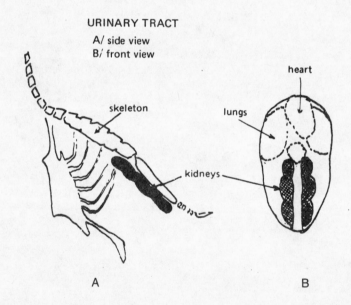

URINARY TRACT
A/ side view
B/ front view

A

B

DISORDERS OF THE KIDNEY(S)

1. Nephritis (most common)
2. Cysts ⎫
3. Tumours ⎬ not so common
4. Degeneration ⎭

1. **Nephritis**

Definition—Non-specific inflammation of the kidney(s)
Causes
   (a) Toxic compounds
   (b) Infectious diseases
   (c) Cold (common in young birds)
   (d) Vit. A deficiency (nutritional)
   (e) Digestive disorders (see Chapter 3)

The disease usually follows a chronic course and birds have been known to survive for as long as two years.

Symptoms and Signs

(i) *Initial or Acute Phase*
   (a) Good appetite but poor condition
   (b) Poor digestion—watery droppings
   (c) Favouring of soft food and greens
   (d) Loves to sit in the sun

(ii) *In-between Phase (or Sub-acute)*
   (a) 'Puffed up' appearance
   (b) Sleeps during the day
   (c) Feels the cold and will snuggle up to other birds for warmth. This is a very important observation and sign, especially in Gouldian Finches who *do not normally* snuggle together
   (d) Loves to sit in the sun
   (e) Death occurs if temperatures drop, i.e. during a sudden cold spell (see Uraemia, page 28)

(iii) *Chronic Phase*
   (a) Severe digestive disorders
   (b) Faeces (not droppings) dull and pasty, yellow colour
   (c) Urine thin and viscid with a raised albumen content
   (d) Stained and fouled ventral area, accompanied by 'tail-whipping'
   (e) Death usually occurs rapidly

Clinical diagnosis is made with difficulty as the symptoms described occur in most digestive and nutritional disorders etc. Usually the disease coincides with a history of exposure to chilly weather etc. or where the chronic symptoms followed an attack of acute uraemia (see Uraemia, below).

Treatment (see First Aid)

Hospitalization, warmth and sulpha-mezathine (see Chapter 11). Prevention is obviously preferred!

Autopsy findings

Kidney or kidneys enlarged 2–3 times their normal size; smooth, shiny and yellow—whitish in colour (fatty degeneration and urate accumulation).

Uraemia (See also Gout)

An increased amount of urea in the bloodstream—which is due to partial or complete shut-down of kidney function. It is as well to mention here that the kidneys are designed to filtrate urine in a **thick** pasty state. *They can perform this function only by virtue of the high body temperature of the bird* ($\pm$ 44° C).

It is only logical to conclude that any condition which causes a drop in body temperature, e.g. draughts, dampness etc., will result in the crystallization of the uric acid in the delicate kidney tubules, leading to a 'shut-down', uraemia and death.

Gout

Gout is due to failure to eliminate nitrogenous waste products (end result of protein metabolism) from the bloodstream through the kidneys, the resultant urate and related substances being deposited in certain areas of the body—i.e. in the joints (articular gout) or in the organs (visceral gout).

Main causes:

(a) Kidney disease.

(b) Diet too rich in protein foods

(c) Diet lacking in protein—in this instance the liver and kidneys are overworked by converting low protein, low-vitamin and high carbohydrate diet into utilizable body substances (going light) resulting in nephrosis (kidney disease) and gout.

2. **Cysts**

May be found on the kidneys and appear as small vesicles (fluid-filled sacs). They are *not* indicative of any specific disease or disorder and do not normally jeopardize the life of the bird.

3. **Tumours**

Rarely seen.

4. **Degeneration**

Some infectious diseases may induce kidney degeneration; kidneys appear soft, friable and yellowish.

REPRODUCTIVE SYSTEMS

In the male it comprises

Two clearly visible yellow-whitish testes located intra-abdominally on each side, just above the kidneys. The very fine tubules (vas deferens) which convey sperm to the cloacal aperature are hardly visible. Except for infertility, the male organs are rarely affected by disorders or disease.

The Female Reproductive System (Refer to diagram page 29)

There is only a left ovary (the right ovary in birds does not grow to maturity), followed by the oviduct. The ovary contains follicles in which arise the ova; each

FEMALE REPRODUCTIVE TRACT

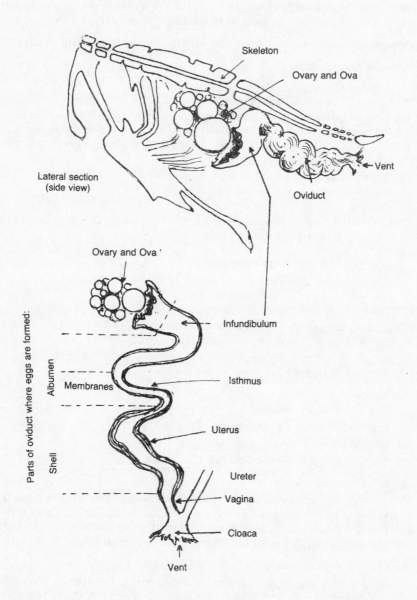

29

ovum (egg), growing in its turn, follows a course down the oviduct until laid. The mechanism determining the rhythm of laying and the successive maturation of each ovum (but never two at the same time) is complex and is governed by hormonal action from the pituitary gland in the brain; the activity of the genital tract (in both sexes) is triggered off by an increase in the length of the day.

Abnormalities and Disorders Associated with the Female Reproductive System

1. **Ovary Abnormalities**

(a) Atrophy (Decrease in size (wasting away))
Causes—Congenital, age or disease
Signs—Evidence of 'male characteristics' and infertility
Prognosis (forecast)—Condition may be temporary if due to hormonal imbalance due to hen laying too many eggs

(b) Cysts (Fluid-filled membrane)
Are not uncommon on the ovaries, oviduct and also seen on the cloaca. They are not a threat to the normal functions.

(c) Ovaritis
Cause(s)—Usually infections originate from the bloodstream, e.g. salmonellosis, typhoid and pullorum.

2. **Salpingitis** (Inflammation of the oviduct)

Cause—Infection may enter via the cloaca or via the bloodstream.

3. **Cloacitis** (Inflammation of the cloaca)

Rare disorder which results in a whitish discharge from the cloaca via the vent, fouling the feathers. Do not confuse with diarrhoea.

LAYING ACCIDENTS

(a) Intra-abdominal laying
(b) Egg and Yolk Retention
(c) Egg Retention or 'Egg Binding'
(d) Rupture of the Oviduct
(e) Prolapse of the Oviduct or Uterus

(a) Intra-abdominal laying
The ovum, instead of entering the oviduct, escapes and falls into the abdominal cavity. If it is non-infected and no more ova escape in this fashion it may remain harmless. However, if an escaped ovum is infected, it can lead to a fatal peritonitis (inflammation of the linings of the organs of the abdominal cavity).

(b) Egg and Yolk Retention
The ovum may stop in the albumen—secreting part of the oviduct. Several ova may accumulate there, surrounded with caseous (cheesy) material; subsequent infection may result in death. These accidents may be due to atony (loss of tone) of

the oviduct caused by fatigue, deficiencies and cold weather or to twisting. Egg retention is more common than an ovum retention.

(c) Egg Retention or 'Egg Binding'

Definition—Hen unable to pass her egg

Causes

    (i) Oviduct fatigue (see (*b*))
    (ii) Malformed or over-sized egg
    (iii) Too young bird or too old
    (iv) Contraction of oviduct and uterus due to drop in temperature
    (v) Obstruction by tumours, secretions etc.
    (vi) Lack of exercise
    (vii) Deficiencies

Symptoms/Signs

    (i) Anxiety/restlessness/puffiness
    (ii) Frequents nest-box
    (iii) Swollen, enlarged cloaca leading to
    (iv) Stiff-legged and straining
    (v) Possible prolapse (see later)
    (vi) If not relieved, death follows within 24 hours.

Diagnosis

Usually made by feeling/seeing swollen and enlarged ventral area plus symptoms as mentioned.

Treatment

Immediate treatment is essential (see First Aid).

    (i) Apply warmth by holding bird above a light bulb for a few minutes (be careful not to burn her).
    (ii) Then turn her on her back and with the thumb and forefinger grasp the abdomen *gently* behind the egg and apply gentle pressure to force egg down toward the vent.

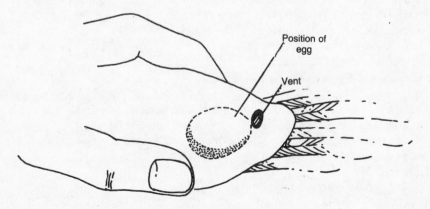

Position of egg

Vent

When the egg comes into view apply some warm olive oil or glycerine on to it and allow the egg to slip back by releasing the pressure.

Pressure is then reapplied and the egg should hopefully be extruded.

If the uterus is attached to the egg (imminent prolapse) due to insufficient relaxation of the sphincter (muscular valve), *do not* force the egg but apply a few drops of tincture of belladona and try again. If, however, prolapse occurs push the uterus gently back into the vent by means of a blunt-nosed eye-dropper and using the same eye-dropper 'inject' some lukewarm saline solution into the cloaca (1 teaspoon of table salt dissolved in a full tumbler of water = saline solution).

(d) Rupture of the Oviduct

Usually a result of egg retention and there is no treatment.

(e) Prolapse of the Oviduct or Uterus

During normal egg-laying, the uterus and part of the oviduct evaginate and then return to their normal position. During difficult laying, they may remain outside and on occasions be complicated by the 'turning out' of the cloaca or even the rectum.

For treatment, see Egg binding. If this condition occurs frequently, deficiencies may be suspected, especially phosphorus deficiency (see Nutrition, Chapter 3).

EGG ABNORMALITIES

(a) Soft-shelled Eggs

(b) Broken Eggs

(c) Infection of the Egg

(d) Infection of the Yolk-sac = omphalitis

(e) Egg-Eating

(f) Infertile Eggs

(a) Soft-shelled Egg(s)

An absence or fragility of the shell is the most common abnormality and is not always due to a calcium deficiency but to—

 (i) fatigue of the reproductive tract

 (ii) oviduct infection

(iii) several vitamin deficiencies

(iv) calcium deficiency and phosphorus deficiency.

The laying of one soft-shelled egg may always happen and if not repeated there is no need for concern unless they are laid by *all* the other hens! This usually is indicative of a nutritional deficiency.

If soft-shelled eggs are noticed in one or a few of the hens, it is best to isolate in case of a *contagious* and local infection being present.

Treatment:

 (i) Try to reduce light duration.

 (ii) Give Terramycin (see Drugs).

(b) Broken Eggs

Not a common occurrence, but if it occurs inject some warm saline solution into the cloaca (see Prolapse). This will aid the hen in passing the broken egg.

(c) Infection of the Egg

Virulent germs (viruses or bacteria) may be present in the egg. Their origin may be in the ovary, in which case the ovum is then infected *before* leaving the ovary (inherited infection), e.g. salmonellosis, pullorum disease and streptococcus.

An egg-shell is porous and is not a barrier against bacteria. Some non-specific bacteria such as colibacilli and also salmonellae can penetrate the shell and the embryo may die as a consequence of the infection or, if the egg hatches, the chick may die from omphalitis (see next heading) or a latent infection of the egg, followed by a fatal disease of the chick.

(d) Infection of the Yolk-sac. Omphalitis—Umbilical Infection

We know that when a chick hatches the yolk-sac remains connected to the intestine and is used as a first source of food by the chick after hatching. Contrary to common belief it has been proved that infection always originates in the egg and not via the yolk-sac and cord. (See previous heading.)

Shell disinfection *before* brooding may be effective. Dip the egg into a solution of 1/1000 quarternary compound—*Note:* The solution *must* always be *warmer* than the egg. After dipping, the egg(s) are left to dry in the air, without rinsing or wiping.

(e) Egg-eating

Only birds deprived of essential nutrients (diet) will do this.

(f) Infertile Eggs

Common Causes:
 (i) Infertility of either sex
 (ii) Old age
 (iii) Mating did not occur
 (iv) Incomplete coition or mating
 (v) Weak hen, e.g. nutritional deficiency
 (vi) Not a true pair (two hens)
 (vii) Eggs chilled before being 'sat on'
(viii) Hereditary disease affecting the development of the embryo.

Note: Seasonal sterility has been known to occur and is therefore a forceful argument against off-seasonal breeding.

CHICKS DEAD IN SHELL

Causes:
 (i) Chilling of eggs, e.g. night fright
 (ii) Conditions too dry or too damp
 (iii) Handling or touching of eggs

(iv) Iodide deficiency

(v) Infection (see Egg abnormalities)

CHICKS DEAD IN NEST

Causes:

(i) Nest too dark—hen unable to feed

(ii) Night fright, e.g. cats, rodents etc.

(iii) Sudden drop in temperature (see below)

(iv) Parents inexperienced or too young, hen is afraid to leave babies to get food

(v) Parasites and infection (see Mites and Nestling Diarrhoea)

(vi) Food—see Nutrition and Poisons

(vii) Death of parents or parents take ill. When chicks are feathering the hen normally ceases to cover them and a sudden drop in temperature will result in chicks dying. Furthermore, when there are only one or two chicks in the nest, they are unable to keep each other warm.

BIRDS NOT BREEDING

Common Causes:

(i) Immaturity

(ii) Old age

(iii) Incompatibility

(iv) Not a true pair

(v) Incorrect environment

(vi) Hormonal imbalance

(vii) Incorrect diet (obesity, malnutrition etc.)

(viii) Disease or disorders

BIRDS LAY BUT DO NOT INCUBATE

Common Causes:

(i) Insecurity

(ii) Disturbances

(iii) Changing of diet

Remedy: Face nest-box opening in different direction. Provide feeling of security be adding foliage around nest site etc.

CHAPTER 6

The Nervous System

The nervous system is, for simplification purposes, made up of the

(1) Central Nervous System—comprising the brain and spinal cord.

(2) The Peripheral Nervous System composed of the Autonomic Nervous System which in turn is divided into the Parasympathetic and Sympathetic systems.

In summary the functions of the nervous system are as follows:

(i) Serves as means of communication between different parts of the body.

(ii) Controls thought and conduct.

(iii) Allows perception of the world around, enables birds to see, to move, to hear and to communicate.

(iv) Control of the internal organs.

(v) Furnishes the body with knowledge of the environment.

(vi) Interprets this knowledge and adjusts to it.

The division of the nervous system is based on difference in function and *not* on an actual anatomical separation.

The division of the Autonomic System into the Sympathetic and Parasympathetic systems is of particular interest as these two systems function antagonistically, i.e. the one works against the other, e.g.

Parasympathetic

(1) Contracts the pupils

(2) Contracts bronchial tubes

(3) Slows and weakens action of the heart

(4) Dilates blood vessels

(5) Increases gut contraction

Sympathetic

(1) Dilates the pupils

(2) Dilates bronchial tubes

(3) Quickens and strengthens the heart's action

(4) Contracts blood vessels

(5) Lessens contraction

As can be seen the sympathetic system is strongly stimulated by pain and unpleasant excitement such as rage and terror. The animal or bird will respond to 'flight or fight'.

DISORDERS OF THE NERVOUS SYSTEM

The disorders listed below are those inducing *abnormal* behaviour of the bird:

Motor hyperexcitability (tremor, convulsions)

Paralysis

However, if the immediate cause of such behaviour is of nervous origin, the causes may be numerous. For example:

35

Nervous troubles following a meningeal or cerebral haemorrhage, usually leading to death

Paralysis caused by compression of the nerves by an egg the female cannot lay

Loss of balance due to lesion(s) of the internal ear

We must add also cases of false paralysis due to pain. When a bird remains on one leg, it may be due to paralysis, but can also be due to pain involved in using the other leg (rheumatism). Some vitamin deficiencies (especially of B1, B2, folic acid, E, D) may induce motor troubles, but these are infrequent. Other possible causes will be studied further:

Any infectious disease may attack the nervous centres and induce troubles; in such cases, the diagnosis may be difficult, for, in cage birds, there is no specific disease causing nervous lesions. Marek's disease, a chickens' disease (also called nervous leucosis), is specific to poultry and is not observed in other species; the possibility of a viral encephalitis cannot be discarded, for day after day new encephalitis viruses are discovered in various animal species. However, no data yet exist on such a disease in canaries and other cage birds.

Intestinal parasites may cause, by their toxins, some nervous disorders but these parasites are infrequent in canaries, though not uncommon in finches and parrot-types.

Poisoning is the usual cause of nervous disorders: paralysis, tremor and convulsions are constant results of poisoning by chlorinated insecticides (D.D.T., Lindane, H.C.H., Dieldrin), which are highly toxic to birds even if only dusted, and without oral absorption. This poisoning is very common.

MENINGEAL AND CEREBRAL HAEMORRHAGES

Meninges are the membranes surrounding (protecting) the brain (cerebrum).

These haemorrhages are the most frequent cause of sudden or rapid deaths in cage birds; they are visible through the skull bone after skinning, when it is possible to see blood effusions under the bone, more or less clearly (see Post-Mortem). Such haemorrhages are usually fatal after some hours, and occur in apparently healthy birds which are suddenly found dead or showing various symptoms such as prostration, tremors, nervous fits, ataxia and lack of co-ordination, leading quickly to death, which occurs within a period of a few to 48 hours.

Meningeal haemorrhage

These haemorrhages have several causes, which may be summarized as follows:

(1) Traumatisms

(2) Individual and internal origin

(3) Infectious origin

(1) Traumatic haemorrhage: follows a blow to the skull, often the consequence of a fight or a fright. In birds in outdoor flights, the passage of a cat, or a bird of prey (or something looking like it) may be the unknown cause of a fright. As we have seen above, the fragility of the skull (induced by calcium or phosphorus or vitamin D deficiencies) makes a haemorrhage more likely to occur and explains the high percentage of sudden deaths occurring in an aviary. In other cases, these accidents are especially common in certain strains, species or families of birds and this may be due to a nervous or fighting disposition. Sometimes, at necroscopy (post-mortem) one may discover a fracture of the skull.

(2) Internal origin: these cases are individual and fortuitous, and generally difficult to distinguish from those traumatic ones in which a lesion of the bone has not occurred. Sometimes, exposure to the sun's rays may cause a cerebral congestion and, in extreme cases, a haemorrhage. (Congestion is the increased accumulation of blood.)

(3) Infectious origin: such haemorrhages are quite frequent in birds with acute canary pox. The lesions occur suddenly in birds showing no external pox lesions but only an extensive internal congestion with internal haemorrhages. In such a case, haemorrhage may be imputed to the viral infection.

Control and prevention: there is no treatment; some mild cases may achieve a spontaneous recovery, but this is infrequent. For many years, bird fanciers have called these accidents 'congestion' or 'cerebral congestion' and advocated, for treatment, darkness, fresh air, a thin trickle of cold water on the head. This results from a confusion between cerebral congestion (by sun's rays) often curable, with the haemorrhage which is an acute and irreversible accident.

As preventive measures, one should:

prevent breeding of all nervous or fighting birds;

insure a good ossification (minerals and vitamins);

avoid all causes of fright.

There are also some non-contagious and strictly individual troubles which heredity may influence—*the neuroses*.

(a) NERVOUSNESS: may occur in certain families and demonstrates different degrees: excited birds—fighting birds—feather plucking—emotional birds. Such birds must not be used for breeding, but in individual cases tranquillizers and sleeping draughts (as reserpine or gardenal) may be used; it is necessary to give the drugs continuously.

(b) EPILEPSY: is not infrequent in cage birds. It shows itself as sudden fits: the bird ruffles its feathers, closes its eyes, trembles, moves its wings and falls without moving, seemingly dead or with some nervous movements. After a short space of time, it becomes conscious and again appears normal.

37

Apart from infrequent cases in which such fits are due to a chronic disease (parasitism), epilepsy is an individual disorder; the fits may become more and more acute and end fatally. The only treatment is a symptomatic one and consists of gardenal sodium salt given continuously (0,20 to 0,30 g per litre of drinking-water).

In some birds, the loss of consciousness if merely caused by a fright, a loud and sudden noise, catching the bird, or emotion (mating, fighting), but does not occur spontaneously; in such cases, the term 'epilepsy' is somewhat improper and it is better to use the term 'emotional syncope'. Loss of consciousness is not preceded by the nervous symptoms which usually precede an epileptic fit. Catching and frightening should be avoided with such birds, for a fit may be fatal.

Generally, it is enough to take the bird into a fresh place and to blow on it.

In some cases, the syncope may be fatal (Syncope = fainting)

(c) HYSTERIA: some researchers have reported cases of hysteria. The bird appears hallucinated and tries to attack or flee from an imaginary enemy. It assumes a threatening posture and turns around in its cage until fully exhausted. Such fits have been noted mainly in parrots.

(d) NEURASTHENIA: Sometimes observed in some birds during acclimatization, following separation of a pair, and, in parrots, a change of owner. The bird is sad and refuses food partially or totally. However, one must be careful not to confuse this with a disease.

(e) SUNSTROKE: a long exposure to the hot rays of the sun may induce a cerebral congestion with sudden torpor, uncertain movements and sometimes nervous disorders; recovery is possible if treatment is started in time before a fatal meningeal haemorrhage occurs. It consists of keeping the bird in a cool place and pouring a thin trickle of cold water on its head. If the trouble is not severe, the bird can be kept in a dark, cool (but not cold) place, with a light diet and fresh drinking-water.

CHAPTER 7

Skin and Feathers

1. Feathers
2. Normal Moult
3. Abnormal Moult
4. Follicular Cysts
5. Feather Abnormalities
6. Feather Plucking
7. Itching
8. Dermatitis
9. Treatment of Skin and Feather Disorders.
10. Uropygitis (pimple) or 'Swollen' Oil Gland

1. FEATHERS

Feathers cover the body of the bird; the small ones serve as a thermal protection, the large wing and tail feathers are used for flight and are replaced when lost under normal conditions. Chemically, the feathers are similar to the hairs of mammals, to the claws and beak; they are of a protein nature, formed principally of keratine, a protein formed of sulphur—containing amino-acids. The flight feathers contain a high proportion of silica.

A marked loss of feathers is observed in birds after the breeding season: it is the moult. This is a normal phenomenon induced by several hormonal secretions, in which the thyroid plays an important role. In some cases (see later) a moult may be induced out of season by a sudden change in feeding, by a disease or any other stress. It is interesting to note that the period of the year in which moult occurs is that in which the day length is *decreasing*. The glandular system of the bird is more susceptible to the *variation* of the day length than to its *true duration*. Following a laying period, the shortening of the day length stops laying and induces the moult.

2. NORMAL MOULT

Normal moult usually occurs without trouble in healthy, normal birds.

Feather-growing requires proteins, especially sulphur-containing amino-acids and in particular, *methionine*, an 'essential' amino-acid which the bird is unable to manufacture and must therefore be available in its food together with all the other essential nutrients. (See Chapter 3.)

3. ABNORMAL MOULT

Partial or extended moults are often observed in cage birds. Usually, they are localized in a small part of the feathering, especially the head and neck. The bird may remain in this condition for several months. The flight feathers are rarely affected except under severe adverse conditions.

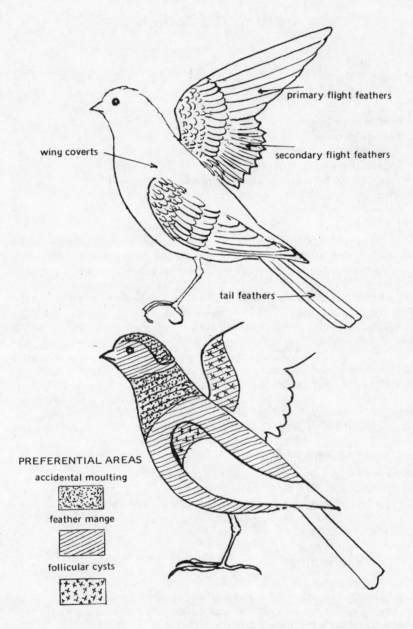

primary flight feathers

wing coverts

secondary flight feathers

tail feathers

PREFERENTIAL AREAS

accidental moulting

feather mange

follicular cysts

By courtesy J. & M. Viguie

Areas of abnormal moult

Another phenomenon observed is a long duration of no growth of new feathers, or of new feathers growing and then falling ('stuck-in-the-moult'). These phenomena are not normally due to deficiencies or mange but to hormonal disorders resulting from abnormal environmental conditions, such as light duration and/or warmth. These conditions are often observed in birds kept indoors in an artificial environment.

It is essential to simulate natural conditions for these 'indoor birds', i.e. long daylight and high temperature in summer, short daylight and low temperature in winter.

It is important to mention here that it is *not advisable* to have a night light in the aviary (except in a hospital cage) for even a weak light is sufficient to 'excite' the pituitary gland (the master-gland which controls all hormonal secretions).

If the lighting is sufficient to allow the title of a newspaper column to be read, it may be enough to act on the birds. Even street lighting may exercise an influence.

Treatment of these abnormal moults is difficult and it is best to ensure that your bird's 'life-rhythm' is as near as possible to nature in one respect, namely daylight duration and, to a lesser extent, temperature.

We can therefore summarize the causes of abnormal moulting or baldness into two main categories, namely—

(1) Congenital or Hereditary
(2) Acquired

(1) Hereditary Baldness

This condition is often observed in crested birds such as pigeons, canaries and Bengalese, etc. In crested birds the crest is a direct inheritance from *only one* parent. The factor in the gene that causes the development of the crest is known as the *lethal dominant factor*. This is clearly demonstrated when a young bird inherits that factor from *one* parent, and it develops a crest; but when it inherits the same *crest-factor* from *both* parents, it dies. In conclusion we see that a crested bird can receive a crest from only one parent, and can pass it on to no more than half its offspring. (See Genetics, Chapter 1.)

The factors 'characterizing' the TYPE of crest are independent of the *crest-factor*, which is responsible only for the development of the crest.

Let us take an example:

'Crest-bred' birds (i.e. birds having one crested parent but NO crest) will *not* produce crested babies but if mated with a crested bird will produce youngsters with crests. Here we see that the presence of *the crest* comes from one parent and

41

the TYPE from the other parent, i.e. the '*crest-factor*' and the *crest-type* are carried in different genes.

To confuse you even more, the 'crest-type' is composed of two factors:

(i) Rosette of feathers

(ii) Bald spot in the middle surrounded by crest. These two factors are permanently linked but the factors governing their relative proportions and development are *not* linked with the crest-gene and so can be inherited separately.

Example:

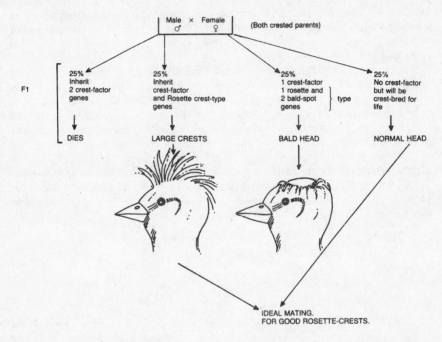

Male × Female
♂   ♀   (Both crested parents)

F1

25% Inherit 2 crest-factor genes → DIES

25% Inherit crest-factor and Rosette crest-type genes → LARGE CRESTS

25% 1 crest-factor 1 rosette and 2 bald-spot genes } type → BALD HEAD

25% No crest-factor but will be crest-bred for life → NORMAL HEAD

IDEAL MATING.
FOR GOOD ROSETTE-CRESTS.

Further examples of baldness are seen in canaries when certain feather-colour types are continuously bred together, leading to very thin, brittle feathers with balding tendencies.

(2) Acquired Causes

(i) Hormonal/Environmental (previously discussed)

(ii) Nutritional deficiencies or excess (previously discussed)

(iii) Physical destruction—by parasites and due to fighting, etc.

(iv) Abnormal conditions—pairing birds when still in baby moult, indiscriminate use of drugs, exhaustion as in excess egg-laying, leading to depletion of body stores.

'French Moult'

No flight or tail feathers or too few or twisted with 'soft shafts'. Causes are believed to be nutritional or hereditary.

4. FOLLICULAR CYSTS

During the moult, when new feathers are growing, one may observe, principally on the wings, some little dry tumours, varying in size; they are formed of keratin and imperfect feathers. This abnormality often appears only at the second moult. The bird attempts to open these cysts and pulls them off, but they re-form. This condition is hereditary and there is no practical treatment.

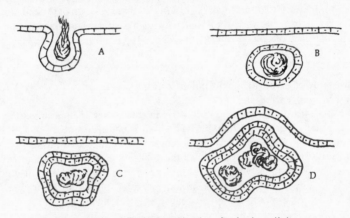

Formation of a follicular cyst (drawing after Lesbouyriès)

5. FEATHER ABNORMALITIES

Various feather abnormalities can occur: brittle feathers, feathers partially losing their barbs, discoloration (grey instead of white). The causes are not always well known; certain deficiencies may be involved especially of pantothenic acid, biotin and folic acid. Though vitaminized treatment is often ineffective, a parasitic cause must not be suspected and any insecticidal treatment is useless. A hormonal or hereditary cause is also possible as in abnormal moult.

6. FEATHER PLUCKING

This is a vicious habit in which the bird plucks the feathers of another bird or its own feathers. It is natural for a bird to look for feathers during brooding time, in order to build its nest. Some females preparing for the next laying period may pluck the feathers of their progeny, and this is a well-known habit.

When feather plucking of other birds is noticed, the cause may be either nervousness or protein or vitamin deficiencies. *If due to deficiencies, the bird* eats *the plucked feathers.*

According to the cause, the treatment will be:
Repulsive preparations on the feathers
Sedatives in food or water (Gardenal–Reserpin)
Vitamins, methionine and proteins of animal origin: insects, eggs, meal-worms (flour beetle larvae).
Separate the pluckers if feather plucking is due to one or two birds.

7. ITCHING

It is common to see birds scratching themselves, more often than is useful for their toilet. Many people tend to impute this itching to external parasites (lice or mange). It is certainly necessary to verify the possible presence of lice, but it must be kept in mind that this scratching has generally an invisible cause and is often related to the moult and to feather growth. In the case of an extended moult, it may persist for a long period, and the growing of sparse feathers induces itching. Insecticides are, of course, ineffective. The skin is often red.

8. DERMATITIS

This name is given to a skin inflammation of various causes. We have already studied the most frequent ones.

A scabby dermatitis has been reported in the canary, beginning at the beak and accompanied by a loss of feathers. The skin is reddish and the bird scratches its beak against the cage rails and the perches. The ailment extends to the neck, then to the wings and the entire body; all the feathers may fall. This ailment has been reported by Sutsmann, who did not find its origin; however, as that was recorded many years ago, when little information was available about B-vitamins and their effects, it is not impossible that the cause was a deficiency.

9. TREATMENT OF FEATHER AND SKIN DISORDERS

It is not always possible to discover the exact cause of the disorder; laboratory examination would be necessary. Fortunately it is possible to try several harmless treatments which eliminate the most common causes:

(1) Application of an insecticidal powder.

(2) If you suspect mange, apply a lotion consisting of a non-toxic insecticidal powder, but never use the medicines for leg scab; they may be harmful if applied on a large area of skin.

These two treatments must be applied once only; if they appear effective, a second application may be made some days later; if ineffective, you must discard lice or mange as a cause of the ailment.

(3) In case of scabs and redness, an external antiseptic may be used. (See Drugs, Chapter 11.)

(4) A varied feed should be given but without fat in excess. However, in cold weather, if the bird is poorly feathered, a piece of fat bacon (fresh piece daily) may be left at its disposal.

(5) Feed should be supplemented with vitamins, minerals and amino-acids.

10. SWOLLEN OIL GLAND
(Uropygitis or Pimple)

The uropygian gland is located at the base of the tail above the vent. It is formed of two lobes and produces a fatty secretion. *Note:* A bird's skin does not possess either sebaceous or sweat glands.

Although there are common suppositions the function of this gland is not understood.

A blocking of the gland can occur.

Treatment—see under Common Emergencies.

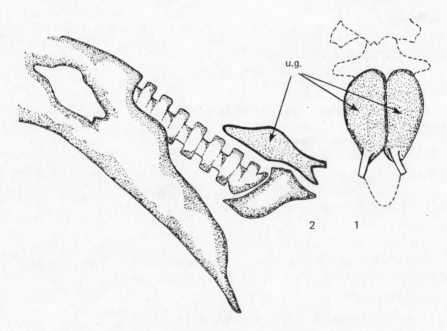

u.g.

2   1

Uropygian gland. (1) From above. (2) Side view.

CHAPTER 8

Sense Organs
(EYES, EARS AND NOSE)

1. EYES

Common disorders are due to minor infections and injuries.

(i) Ulcerative Keratitis ⎫
(ii) Iritis due to paracoli ⎭ observed in canaries

(iii) Lens opacity (cataract)−old age!

Other indirect causes are due to:

(i) Respiratory disease

(ii) Sinusitis

(iii) Common cold (coryza)

(iv) Avitaminosis A; i.e. Vitamin A deficiency

(v) Pox.

Treatment:

Infections and injuries are best treated with Chloromycetin (Parke-Davis) eye ointment. Other indirect lesions−treat the cause but apply palliative treatment to the eyes. Palliative = treating the symptoms and not the cause.

2. EARS

Our main concern is with disorders and infections of the inner ear, in which are situated the organs of balance (semicircular canals). Common disorders are:

(i) Vertigo

(ii) Torticollis

Common infections are due to viruses, bacteria and mites, e.g. Canary pox virus and red mites.

Symptoms:

(i) Abnormal positioning of the head (red mite)

(ii) Staggering

(iii) Loss of equilibrium

(iv) Keeps its head bent or turned up, sometimes with swaying movements.

Treatment:

If due to red mites− give 0,5 parts sulphaquinoxaline (Embazin) to 1 000 parts of drinking-water for 5 days.

3. THE NOSE

Common infections are Sinusitis and Red Mite

Symptoms:

(i) Sinusitis—Usually in conjunction with the eyes; there is congestion and discharge through the nasal cavities. Treat with nasal oil.

(ii) Red Mite—Bird is seen trying to dislodge the 'irritation' with its foot. There is also congestion—discharge. Treatment—As for red mite in ears but preferably use Pyrethrin aerosol spray (see Red Mites).

CHAPTER 9

Infectious and Contagious Diseases

Since infections play such a large part in the production of ill health it is essential to have a knowledge of the different types of organisms which may cause disease and of how these agents gain access to the body.

In addition, a knowledge of treatment is essential both in regard to the general management and specific measures to be taken, such as the sulphonamide drugs and antibiotics (chemotherapeutic agents). Without fear of contradiction it will suffice to say that the old adage of 'Prevention is better than cure' is the order of the day. Infectious and contagious diseases are caused by—

1. Viruses, Rickettsiae and Mycoplasma

2. Bacteria

3. Fungus

4. Parasites and Protozoan (Internal or External)
  (i) Worms (Helminths)
 (ii) Insects and Acarids

1. Viruses, Rickettsiae and Mycoplasma
    (a) Newcastle Disease ('Fowl plague') (Pneumoencephalitis)
    (b) Avian Pox or Diphtheria
    (c) Mycoplasma Disease

2. Bacteria
    (a) Salmonellosis
    (b) Colibacillosis
    (c) Pseudo Tuberculosis
    (d) Pasteurellosis (Fowl Cholera)
    (e) Tuberculosis
    (f) Staphylococcal and Streptococcal Infections
    (g) Corynebacteriosis

3. Fungus
    (a) Aspergillosis sp.
    (b) Thrush (Moniliasis)

4. Parasites and Protozoan (Parasites may be either internal or external).
    (a) Coccidiosis or Isosporosis
    (b) Ornithosis
    (c) Spirochaetosis
    (d) Trypanosomiasis
    (e) Toxoplasmosis

(f) Worms (Internal Parasites)
    (i) Round worms or Nematodes
    (ii) Tapeworms or Cestodes
    (iii) Gape Worm

(g) Insects (External parasites)
    (i) Body and Feather Lice
    (ii) Mosquitoes

(h) Acarids (mites)
    (i) Red Mite or Dermanyssus
    (ii) Ornithonyssus sylviarium
    (iii) Argas
    (iv) Respiratory Mites (internal parasite)
    (v) Manges

Sources of Infection

(a) Healthy Birds —e.g. during the incubation period of a disease.
(b) 'Carriers' —healthy birds can be 'carriers' of a particular disease without showing any symptoms of the disease.
(c) Other animals —earthworms, snails and slugs, mice etc. See Gape worm and enteritis.

Spread of Infection

Either by direct contact (Contagious) or via indirect sources (Infectious). The following are some of the means by which infections can be spread.
(a) Droplet—coughing, sneezing
(b) Dust—e.g. aspergillosis
(c) Ingestion—contaminated food and water
(d) Direct Invasion—e.g. via conjunctiva, mucous membranes and skin, e.g. mites
(e) Contamination of wounds—Bacterial usually.

General Symptoms and Signs of Infection

(a) Loss of appetite but *increased thirst*
(b) Rise in body temperature—shivering, increased breathing rate and heart rate
(c) Puffed feathers
(d) Lowered resistance—leads to further attack by other organisms
(e) Immobility

General Principles of Treatment

Chemotherapeutic agents, i.e. antibiotics etc.
Multi-vitamin supplement
Warmth and Rest
Isolation if possible (see 'Hospital Cage' and First Aid).

1. VIRAL AND RICKETTSIAL DISEASES

It is fortunate that viral diseases—with the exception of colds—are not common in finches and waxbills, for they are usually fatal. Diagnosis and treatment of these diseases are best left to the specialists.

Only two diseases in this category are of importance:

(a) Newcastle Disease ('Fowl plague') (Pneumoencephalitis)

Can occur in canaries, sparrows and other cage passeriforms. Symptoms—non-specific respiratory troubles—nervous disorders, diarrhoea. *Highly contagious.*

(b) Avian Pox or Diphtheria (Contagious Catarrh, Roup, Canker)

Symptoms—Red pimples develop on the eyelids, nostrils and legs. Gradually increase in size during two weeks and are then covered by a darkish scab. Conjuctivitis often occurs.

Treatment: Best undertaken by veterinary surgeon. There is no treatment available and prevention of the disease is important.

Pox lesions

(c) Mycoplasma Disease (Mycoplasmosis or Chronic Respiratory Disease (CRD) and Catarrh)

A highly contagious disease affecting the Respiratory System. Mycoplasma organisms have similarities both to bacteria and to the organisms known as rickettsiae.

Symptoms

Vary in intensity and may extend from noisy breathing to dramatic fits or suffocation, accompanied by 'whistling' breathing sounds. Frequent swallowing (cf. Gapes, Aspergillosis). 'Smacking' respiratory sounds, especially at night, are frequent. Sero-mucous nasal discharge (catarrh) plus pharyngitis is also present. Course of the disease is usually chronic and not fatal but the bird's general condition is poor, 'Going Light'. Secondary bacterial infection will lead to death.

The above *symptoms* are not uncommon in Gouldian Finches.

Diagnosis: is difficult for it can well be confused with Acariasis (see Mites) which has identical symptoms.

Post-mortem Findings: Mucus in trachea plus congestion. The air-sacs are sometimes filled with 'cheesy' deposits.

Treatment

Chloramphenicol, Mycosan-t and Furazolidone. It is best to give two of the antibiotics *together* for a period of 5–6 days. If the first period gives no improvement then acariasis must be suspected and an aerosol treatment (see under Acariasis) undertaken. If a total or partial recovery results from the first treatment, the treatment *must* be continued over two or three further periods to avoid relapses. The antibiotic of choice is determined by the results obtained. However, treatment is often unsatisfactory.

2. BACTERIA

The symptoms of bacterial infections (see page 49 for General Symptoms and Signs) are always the same, which makes correct diagnosis difficult. Accurate diagnosis is usually made by laboratory studies, i.e. cultures etc. Diarrhoea may be associated and in cases of bacterial enteritis the droppings may be blood-stained, cf. faeces is *not* blood-stained in coccidiosis (see later).

Treatment

Bacterial infections can all be treated, unlike viruses, with antibiotics. Chloramphenicol is best. Terramycin as second choice. Period of treatment 6–8 days.

(a) **Salmonellosis** (Paratyphoid or Enteric Fever)

Most frequently encountered bacterial disease in cage birds, except for colibacillosis. It is most commonly found in pet shops etc. where the birds are confined and are in continuous contact with other birds—bought and sold. It is strongly advised to *quarantine all new birds for at least 10 days* prior to their introduction to an established stock.

Diagnosis—only by a properly equipped laboratory.

(b) **Colibacillosis** (Nestling Diarrhoea in young birds) E. coli.

Most common cause of death of chicks between the 6th and 8th day after hatching and is due to *stale or mouldy food.*

Symptoms and Signs

Chicks develop a thin watery diarrhoea which dampens and fouls the nest. This in turn results in the breast feathers of the hen (most commonly) becoming matted as if she has been 'sweating'. (*Note:* birds *do not* sweat.) The hen, if examined, is seen to have a greyish, stringy diarrhoea.

E. coli may also give rise to a septicaemia; septic arthritis—'bumble-foot', and chronic air sacculitis.

Treatment

If noticed in time—move the chicks into a clean, dry nest. Chloramphenicol or Furazolidone given to potential parents at least 5 days before hatching and until the young birds reach 10–12 days of age. Use the antibiotics alternatively to avoid possible resistance.

51

Here can be seen another typical example of prevention, i.e. clean food.

(c) **Pseudo Tuberculosis**

(d) **Pasteurellosis (Fowl Cholera)**

(e) **Tuberculosis**   Rare and not often

(f) **Staphylococcal and Streptococcal Infections**   seen.

(g) **Corynebacteriosis**

3. FUNGUS (Mould)

(a) Aspergillosis sp.

Most common causative organism is A. fumigatus, present as the mould or dust on food. The disease caused is a pulmonary (lung) or generalized mycosis (mycosis is a lesion caused by mould growing in tissue).

Symptoms

Usually an acute disease ending in death within 2 to 6 days. The 'patient' manifests all the signs of an acute infection with added respiratory signs such as gasping (cf. Gapes C.R.D. Acariasis) for air. Its head may hang between its feet or drawn back. Death can be directly caused by the toxins of the mould (mycotoxicosis).

Post-mortem Findings

Greenish and whitish mycosis in lungs, trachea and air-sacs confirms the diagnosis.

Treatment

Is unsatisfactory. Questionable results obtained by giving 3 drops (into the mouth) of potassium iodide (Lugols Soln. 10%) for a long period!

Prevention

Again this is the best cure; so do not feed your birds on stale or mouldy feed and keep humidity (which favours mould growth) down. If the mould is noticed, spraying or painting with a copper sulphate solution is effective. It is worth while to repeat again that any bird with respiratory disease must be treated at once because a generally weakened condition (resistance), especially of the respiratory tract, always favours secondary infection, be it viral, bacterial or fungal.

(b) Thrush (Moniliasis)

Virtually unknown, but can be induced by prolonged or excessive use of chemotherapeutic agents.

Symptoms: Persistent diarrhoea.

Treatment: Mycostatin or Nystatic (anti-fungal agents)

4. PARASITES AND PROTOZOAN

These causative organisms' sizes range from microscopically small to those easily visible (macroscopic):

(a) Coccidiosis or Isosporosis
(b) Ornithosis (Psittacosis or 'Parrot Fever')
(c) Spirochaetosis
(d) Toxoplasmosis
(e) Trypanosomiasis
(f) Worms
(g) Insects
(h) Acarids (Mites)

(a) Coccidiosis or Isosporosis

Symptoms: In finches and other small birds it presents itself as a chronic and mild disease, and is not commonly seen (Ref. Viguie). It presents similar symptoms to those of enteritis.

Diagnosis: Made by microscopic examination of faeces.

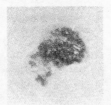

Watery droppings in
case of coccidiosis

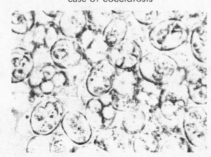

Coccidiae oocysts (microscopic amplification)

Treatment: Sulphamezathine 5 ml to 1 litre of H_2O given for 3 days; stopped for 2 days and then continued for a further 3 days. 3 : 2 : 3 regime. Fresh solution to be made up daily. Follow manufacturer's instructions carefully.

53

Parakeet ascaris

Ascarides in the intestine

Tapeworm segments
squashed between
2 sheets of glass

Capillaria egg

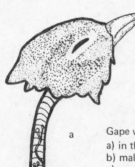

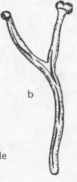

Gape worms
a) in the trachea
b) male and female
c) egg

PARASITIC WORMS

(b) **Ornithosis** (Psittacosis) (Laryngotracheitis and Rhinitis) (Parrot Fever).

Symptoms and Signs: watery conjunctivitis, swollen eyelids and nasal discharge which can lead to blindness. Contagious and is not caused by a virus as previously thought but by a rickettsia-like organism called Chlamydia.

The disease may follow an acute pattern followed by rapid death or a slow (chronic) evolution form.

Epidemiology: Commonly carried by pigeons and through their dried droppings and feathers spreads via the air.

Treatment: Terramycin is antibiotic of choice. Chloramphenicol as standby. Recovery usually within ± 8 days. But *birds which survive the disease may become carriers.* It is best to destroy the bird.

(c) **Spirochaetosis**

(d) **Trypanosomiasis**

(e) **Toxoplasmosis**

Rarely seen in finches and waxbills. Treatment same as for *(a)* and *(b)*

(f) **Worms** (Internal Parasites)

In birds, worms are commonly parasites of the intestine. Their occurrence in small birds, especially Grass Finches, is common but not uncommon in parrot and parakeet-type birds.

Diagnosis: Microscopical examination of faeces taken at random; break up faeces in a little H_2O, add a trace of methylene blue. Place in a petri-dish or watch-glass and examine in strong light for worms or segments.

Birds kept on open ground aviaries are more likely to become infested with worms. Especially if fowls, game birds etc. have been kept previously. Worm eggs can live for lengthy periods in the soil. Vectors are flies, beetles, ants, earthworms, snails, slugs and, of course, other birds.

Three Main Groups (See page 54)

(i) Round Worms (Nematodes) Capillaria (thread worm) and Ascaris

(ii) Tapeworms (Cestodes)

(iii) Gape Worm (Red worm or forked worm)

Treatment Programme: (Medicaments are termed *Vermifuge*)

Remove all water from the aviaries or cages at about 16h00. Make up the specific treatment (see below) and do not return the medicated drinking water until the following morning at about 10h00. The birds will be very thirsty and will normally drink enough of the medication to eradicate the parasite(s). Leave the medicated water for *one whole day* before replacing with fresh, clean water.

(i) *Round Worms or Nematodes* (Ascarid)

Use Tetramisole, repeated at intervals of 4 to 6 weeks for capillaria and ascarid infestation. Dosage 5 ml of a 3% solution per litre of water during *one day only*.

For ascarid infestation only use 'Antepar' (piperazine adipate). Dosage of 2–3 g per litre of water for *one day*. Tramisol is, however, preferred

(ii) *Tapeworms or Cestodes*

(1) Lintex—Disolve 1 tablet in 30 cc H_2O for *one day only*; or (2) Droncit (Bayer)—crush 1 × 5 mg tablet over soaked seed for one day only.

(iii) *Gape Worm* (See page 54)

Approximately 15 mm long and clearly visible in the trachea. Although not common in finches, it can occur. It attaches itself to the mucosal lining of the trachea and sucks blood. This causes an inflammation which can lead to obstruction. It can also invade the air-sacs.

Symptoms: Bird is dull and listless and sleeps during the day. Feathers are carried loosely. Breathing may be 'asthmatic' at night. Every few minutes, while at rest, the bird thrusts its head forward, opens its beak wide, and works its neck as if in an attempt to swallow something (cf. acariasis). Hence the name 'Gapes'.

Treatment and Prevention: Avoid feed becoming contaminated with soil. Treatment as with acariasis, or Thiabendazole given during 8 days in the food. *Note:* The earthworm and snail are intermediate hosts and birds such as Robins, Blackbirds etc. are prone to this infection.

Insects and Acarids

Insects and acarids are EXTERNAL parasites: the only exception being the respiratory mite which lives in the trachea.

(g) **Insects**—Have *six* legs

(1) Body and feather lice.
(2) Mosquitoes.

(1) *Body and Feather Lice*

These parasites are more of an irritant to the adult bird than a threat to its health for they (the parasites) feed on dead skin and feathers. They are *not* blood sucking and do not willingly leave their host (cf. red mites). However, these parasites can cause undue disturbance and irritation in young birds and so interfere with their much-needed sleep and rest.

Heavily infested birds will develop severe dermatitis (skin inflammation), feather destruction and consequent loss. Under these circumstances the hen(s) will abandon the chicks.

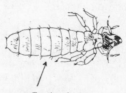

Feather Louse

Life Cycle. The lice lay their eggs (nits) on the shafts of the flight feathers; the larvae hatch and eat their way across the web at right angles to the shaft, leaving the feathers dry and brittle.

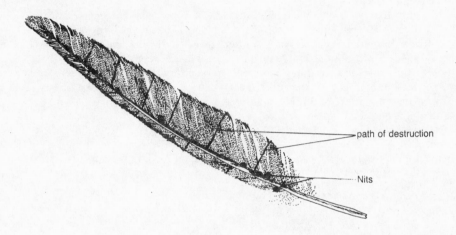

Prevention and Treatment. As mentioned, lice usually occur in conjunction with mites and treatment is aimed at the destruction of both.

Once a week spray entire quarters, including nest boxes (not those with eggs or chicks) with Rekotox-P or Lopis Dog Aerosol. (contains Pyrethrins and Carbaryl). Individual birds are dusted with 5% Carbaryl Powder (Karbadust). Bird bath should always be available during warm hours of the day *only*.

(2) *Mosquitoes*

Mosquitoes attack the exposed areas of the body such as the feet and the area surrounding the eyes, leaving nasty sores, which as a result of secondary infection, heal very slowly. Often this can lead to blindness or the loss of a toe or toes (see Feet). It is interesting to note that young birds are more prone to attack by mosquitoes because they are afraid to leave the perch during the night, whereas the adult birds will protect themselves by perching on the ground/floor and cover their feet.

The young bird's only defence to ward off an attack is to kick at the enemy with its free foot and create a faint stamping noise.

(h) **Acarids** (mites)—have *eight* legs

  (i) Red Mite (Dermanyssus gallinae)
 (ii) Ornithonyssus sylviarium
(iii) Argas
 (iv) Respiratory Mites
  (v) Manges

Red mite →

(i) *Red Mite or Dermanyssus*

0,4 to 0,7 mm in length. It is pale yellow coloured but red after feeding on blood, during the night. They are often present in such large numbers that they can destroy a chick directly, by virtually sucking it dry, or indirectly by causing the hen to abandon her nest.

Red mite does not live on the birds. During the day it remains hidden in crevices, under roosts etc. At night it leaves its place of hiding to attack the birds. Detection requires a careful inspection and is often revealed by the mite's droppings appearing as a grey powder (very much like powdered pepper). It is rapidly killed by the sun's rays and by using a wettable powder containing 85% of carbaryl suspended in water (2,5 gm per litre) and spraying all parts of the cage or aviary. This treatment is effective for ± 3 months. A 5% carbaryl powder may be applied to the birds and their nests (see Lice).

Sulphaquinoxaline (Embazin®) (1 teaspoonful/litre) or (0,25 g per litre H_2O) given
in the drinking-water for 4–6 days has a systemic action and kills the red mite which bites the treated birds.

(ii) *Ornithonyssus sylviarum*

Similar to red mite but tends to live more on the bird. Treat same as for red mite.

(iii) *Argas*

6–10 mm in length and common in hot and temperate climates but rather infrequent in well-maintained aviaries and cages. Habits and treatment as for red mite.

(iv) *Respiratory Mites* (0,5 mm long)

In small-bird species like passarines, canaries and small psittacines, they appear as virulent parasites, present in the trachea, bronchi, air-sacs, lungs and even on the surface of the liver.

They are rather common in Gouldian Finches suffering from 'respiratory troubles'.

Their life-cycle is not known, for only adult mites are seen in the trachea and it is possible, therefore, that the parasite spends a part of its life elsewhere.

Symptoms: These are indistinguishable from those of respiratory diseases, which are more common. Painful and noisy breathing, frequent attempts at swallowing (see C.R.D. and Gapes). The course of the disease can be slow (chronic) or acute and fatal if the mites are present in high numbers.

Respiratory mite under the microscope   Respiratory mites in the trachea

Diagnosis: Only by post-mortem where the mites are usually visible to the naked eye. The trachea may also be congested with mucus.

Prevention and Treatment: Pyrethrin aerosols (Lopis Bird aerosol) give excellent and rapid results in just two applications to the bird in a cage covered with a cloth. Karbadust® is another effective treatment.

(v) *Manges*

These mites cause leg scab and feather mange. Most common is leg scab or 'scaly feet' which affects the unfeathered parts of the legs. The scales of the feet are raised by a whitish dry matter. The legs are rough and enlarged (not to be confused with 'Bumble-foot'—see nutritition) and known as 'Tassel-foot'. The course is slow, and transmission is by contact.

Treatment: Use Johnson's Scaly Leg remedy or, even simpler, soak the affected areas with some olive oil. Repeat three days later and the scales should now be removed very carefully. Remember to clean and disinfect all perches etc. Mange mites also affect the nostrils and extend around the eyes (seen in budgerigars).

'scaly foot'   'scaly face'

'Feather Mange' and Body Mange

The term 'body mange' is preferred because it is a disease of the skin which causes the feathers to fall from the infected areas. However, it never causes the flight feathers to fall, but only the small feathers. (Not to be confused with accidental moulting.)

Diagnosis: Examination of the affected areas reveals some fatty and yellowish coloured scabs on the skin or on the base of the feathers. The mites are present in these scabs.

Treatment: Carbaryl suspension or ointment applied to the affected areas. It must be borne in mind that this disease is uncommon and an accurate diagnosis is essential.

Body mange

Leg Scab Acarid

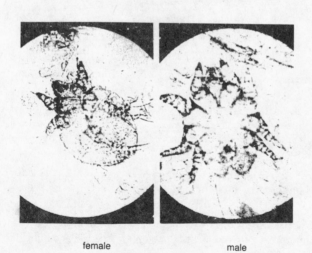

female   male

Feather mange acarids

EXTERNAL PARASITES

CHAPTER 10

Chemical and Physical Injuries

(Common Emergencies and First Aid)

FIRST AID

This gives every bird a fighting chance to recover.

Basic Requirements:

  (i) A 'hospital cage' closed on three sides.

 (ii) Heat (18°C–25°C) Provided by 2 × 20 W *Frosted* bulbs situated at each end, inside or closely hanging outside the cage. This light must be left on for 24 hours. It does not affect the 'patient's' sleep and it allows access to the vital food and water at all times.

(iii) Generous and easily accessible food supplies.

 (iv) Liquid appetizers, i.e. vitamins and minerals.

  (v) Antibiotics, if indicated, to help prevent secondary infections.

 (vi) All perches to be removed.

(vii) Last, but not least, REST. Do not disturb the 'patient' unnecessarily.

CHEMICAL INJURIES (Toxins or Poisons)

(1) Carbon Monoxide—Cage birds may be poisoned by very small quantities of CO in the air.

Sources: Gas stoves and combustion engines.

(2) Domestic Insecticides (Poisons)—Their essential active ingredients are chlorinated compounds (D.D.T., Dieldrin).

Symptom: Manifest as nervous disorders.

Treatment: Gardenal 0,20 g per litre H_2O + vitamins + high doses of calcium chloride 1 g per 100 ml H_2O.

(3) Emission of unknown gas(es) in the kitchen following cooking of meat in 'roto grills' has resulted in sudden death of birds housed in the kitchen.

PHYSICAL INJURIES AND ACQUIRED ABNORMALITIES

(1) FRACTURES

(a) Skeleton, Feet and Wings

Birds are very prone to head, wing and foot injuries and prevention of these accidents or minimizing their occurrence is obviously preferred. Aviaries should be checked thoroughly for odd pieces of string, wire etc. in which a bird may become entangled or strangulated.

61

SKELETON

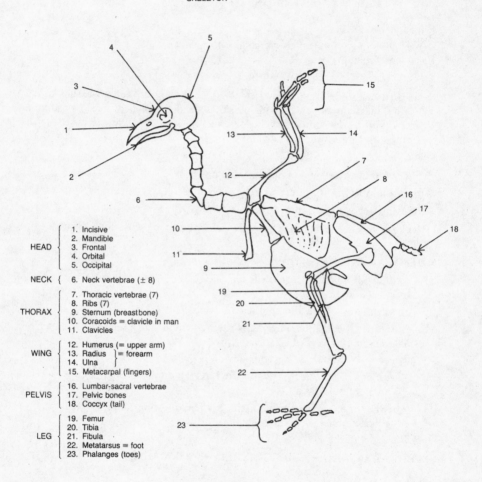

HEAD
{
1. Incisive
2. Mandible
3. Frontal
4. Orbital
5. Occipital
}

NECK { 6. Neck vertebrae (± 8)

THORAX
{
7. Thoracic vertebrae (7)
8. Ribs (7)
9. Sternum (breast bone)
10. Coracoids ≡ clavicle in man
11. Clavicles
}

WING
{
12. Humerus (≡ upper arm)
13. Radius } ≡ forearm
14. Ulna
15. Metacarpal (fingers)
}

PELVIS
{
16. Lumbar-sacral vertebrae
17. Pelvic bones
18. Coccyx (tail)
}

LEG
{
19. Femur
20. Tibia
21. Fibula
22. Metatarsus ≡ foot
23. Phalanges (toes)
}

Wing Fracture(s)

Very difficult to treat in small birds for the resentment shown by the struggles of the bird aggravates the injury and, secondly, there is no way of affixing a cast or splint without doing more harm than good. The best course to follow is to place the bird in a hospital cage (see First Aid) (remove all perches first) and to observe the droop of the injured wing. If the wing hangs in a graceful droop, go about your business; leave the patient undisturbed for the next ten days and there is a good chance that the bird will not be crippled. If the wing hangs at an awkward angle, it must be folded against the bird's side in as natural a position as possible, and then held in place by passing a narrow strip of adhesive tape twice around the body in such a manner as to leave the other wing free. These birds always end up crippled.

Leg Fractures

Leg fractures located in the femur or tibia cannot be set. Only fracture(s) of the metatarsus can be set and held in place by placing the shank in a plastic straw (slit along its length) and tied with thread. The tube must be loose enough to allow for swelling. The bird's injured foot is now put in a foot sling, which keeps the foot in the natural, normal position (see diagram). The wings must be kept free.

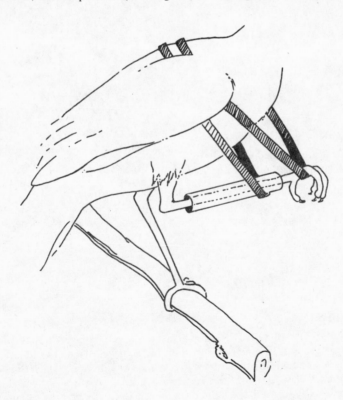

Broken Toes

These injuries usually go undiscovered and the injury is not serious if it involves the front toes. It usually heals without treatment. However, if injury occurs to the back toe it often causes the back claw to become stiff. When this happens to a female, her breeding career is over. Males can sometimes manage to copulate but it is more the exception than the rule.

Slipped Claw

This condition is the result of nest injury. It is a dislocation of the back claw, which usually occurs when there are but one or two chicks in the nest. The hen in her efforts to keep the chicks warm covers them too closely. In moving around the chick gets one of its back claws slipped forward between the front toes and, because of the weight of the hen, is unable to rise up and get the claw back into the correct position. It takes only a short time for the claw to grow into the 'abnormal' position and by the time it leaves the nest all voluntary control over the affected claw has been lost. The bird can no longer grasp the perches.

A.

B.

Sketch A illustrates slipped claw
Sketch B illustrates method of treatment

Leave adhesive tape or open celluloid leg band in position for several weeks. Care must be taken not to bind the leg too tightly. Chronic cases, with a little patience, can be corrected by progressive banding of the claw over a period of many weeks.

Skull Fractures

These are usually fatal.

(2) FEET AND BEAK

Overgrown Claws

Usually due to lack of wear. Perches should preferably be oval and not round. Regular inspection and trimming if necessary are required. Claws: Ordinary nail clippers are good enough. Be careful not to sever the blood vessels which run down the centre of each claw for about half its normal length. They are easily visible. If they are accidentally severed, the lighted tip of a cigarette can be used to cauterize

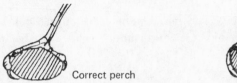

Correct perch

Incorrect perch

the bleeding. If you are a non-smoker (good for you), then ordinary household hydrogen peroxide or iron sulphate (Monsel's Salts) can be used to arrest bleeding.

Overgrown Beak

Usually the sides and point of the upper mandible become overgrown. The point of the beak is snipped off at an angle from both sides so as not to leave it blunt. Care must be taken not to cut the corium or 'quick'. The sides are cut by resting the point of the beak on a suitable hard surface (e.g. wooden table), slipping a thin sharp knife inside the mouth and cutting downwards toward the point of the bill and *not* toward the corners of the mouth. 'Scaly beak' of budgerigars is due to advanced infestation of Knemidocoptes. Euthanasia is treatment of choice.

Prevention: Place some fine sandpaper around the perches.

Swollen Feet ('Bumble-foot')

See also Leg Disorders. 'Bumble-foot' is an abscess found on the toes and ball of the feet of birds.

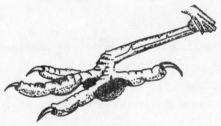

'Bumble-foot'

Causes: Nutritional (gout, arthritis) insect bites, chronic bacterial infections or diphtheric lesions, lack of exercise or injury.

Treatment: Depends on correct diagnosis—drastic excision followed by application of an antibiotic powder and plaster-coverage.

Leg Scab

A common condition which is discussed under Parasitic Infections.

Reddish and Swollen Legs

Symptoms: Legs are congested and swollen

65

Causes
 (i) Excess fat in diet, especially rancid fat of animal origin, i.e. C.L.O.
 (ii) Excessive use of products used to colour red canaries based on residues from palm oil extraction.

Treatment
 (i) Correction of cause.
 (ii) High doses of vitamin E, e.g. wheat germ oil.

Dry Gangrene of the Legs

Symptoms: The toe becomes dark, dries and falls off. This disorder may involve one toe or a part of a toe, and often all the toes of a leg are lost, one after the other, reducing the leg to a stump.

Causes: Not clearly understood but possibly—
 (i) Circulatory—constriction of the blood vessels
 (ii) Feeding ergoted seeds
 (iii) Microbial (non-specific).

Treatment: If due to circulation, a treatment with citro-flavanoids or with rutin may be effective. Also apply a topical antibiotic ointment such as Panalog ointment (Squibb).

Red and Painful Legs

Symptoms: Leg is red but without swelling. Bird stands on its good leg, holding its painful leg high.

Causes: Possibly rheumatism.

Treatment: Local application of cortisone plus antibiotic ointment such as Synalar-N, Quadriderm, Panalog etc.

Gout (see Kidneys, Chapter 5)

Symptoms: Swollen feet joints, tender and painful. Enlarged abdomen usually present.

Differential Diagnosis: Scaly Leg, injury, insect bites etc. See other disorders.

Treatment: Correction of diet (if dietary in origin).

OTHER COMMON AILMENTS AND DISORDERS

Swollen Oil Gland
 (Pimple) (see Skin and Feathers).

Causes: Most commonly due to blockage of the duct by hardened secretions due to lack of exercise or lack of bathing facilities.

Treatment: Gentle pressure or repeated massaging with olive oil. A matchstick head can be used to assist in removing the blockage. Apply a topical disinfectant. (See Chapter 11.)

Fits (see Nervous System)

Causes: Brain haemorrhage, lack of exercise, nutritional deficiency, over-exposure to sun and infectious diseases.

Treatment: Based on correct diagnosis. Try dipping head into cold water for a split second. Remove cause.

Egg Binding (see Reproductive System)

Sour Crop

Causes: Nutritional or Infectious

Treatment: Add 1 teaspoon Enos to one litre of water.

Crop Impaction

Symptoms: Enlarged crop plus distress.

Causes: More common in chicks due to swallowing something that will not pass through the crop (obstruction). This causes pressure on the trachea (windpipe) and can lead to suffocation.

Treatment:
(a) Removal of impacted material can be attempted by injecting a little warm saline solution into the crop (through the skin) and working the impacted material back up through the mouth; or
(b) Surgically—A delicate operation best left to a specialist.

Shock/Heart Attacks/Haemorrhage

Causes:
 (i) Rough handling
 (ii) Injury
 (iii) Severe infections
 (iv) Poisoning
 (v) Sudden frights

GENERAL WOUNDS (Scratches, Cuts, Bruises of the Skin and Deeper Tissues)

Small areas of damaged skin require little more than bathing with a weak antiseptic solution or with weak saline solution (1 teaspoonful of common household salt to half litre water). If the extent of the wound cannot be determined, it is best to cut or to pluck all the feathers around it. Cleanse the wound and apply an anti-bacterial cream or spray. Do not use ointments, they foul the feathers, and do *not* cover body wounds with bandages or other dressings. Remember open wounds heal quickly and can be cleaned and observed without unduly disturbing the 'patient'. Antibiotics should be reserved for deep and/or infected wounds.

CHAPTER 11

Treatment–Drugs, their Uses, Actions and Indications

It is not in the scope of this chapter, or of the book for that matter, to list all the drugs available. The purpose here is to give you certain basic guidelines and examples of only a few drugs, for once you know what they are intended for it surely narrows down your 'shopping list'.

Remember, too, that larger birds are easier to treat, for most of the medicines are available in capsule or tablet form and can be given directly per mouth. Needless to say, the case is not so with the smaller birds. They are best treated via their drinking-water or food.

BASIC PRINCIPLES OF TREATMENT

As mentioned before, the treatment chosen should be the result of a *correct* clinical diagnosis which has been carried out in the most objective way possible or after a laboratory examination. Fortunately with the modern drugs at our disposal, the distinction between salmonellosis, fowl typhoid and colibacillosis is of no importance. The treatment is the same with broad-spectrum antibiotics.
Rules to observe:

  (i) Do not combine various treatments unless indicated.
  (ii) Do not apply them at too short an interval–the chosen treatment should be allowed to take its course, usually 5–8 days.
  (iii) Follow the manufacturer's instructions closely.
  (iv) Allow at least 2 or 3 days for results.
  (v) Do not give drugs as a preventative measure unless instructed by the manufacturer.
  (vi) Not all bacteria are harmful. The natural 'flora' is compatible with good health. Bacterial flora in the gut is essential for vitamin B and K production. Because antibiotics are *not* selective in their fight against bacteria, destruction of the harmless and necessary 'flora' in the gut will lead to a deficiency in these vitamins and enteritis and haemorrhage can occur. Prolonged therapy is harmful.
  (vii) Antibiotics usually act more effectively in a healthy bird, which is better equipped to cope than a sick bird with a lowered resistance. Early diagnosis is essential.

With a sick bird, one should not necessarily choose antibiotics or sulphonamides. It has been proved that 95% of cases are of a hepatic (liver), intestinal or kidney nature. Consequently it is for this reason that the 'insignificant' correctors of unbalanced diets are most important.

Please note that the above rules by no means refer to vitamins, minerals or other 'diet correctors', the regular use of which is normal.

68

Fortunately, for us, there exist many polyvalent and broad-spectrum medicines that very often give satisfactory results for a large number of diseases as will be seen later.

MODES OF TREATMENT

(a) Direct Administration

(b) Indirect Administration (Preferred)

(a) **Direct Method**

(i) Injection

(ii) By mouth

(i) *Injection:* Not common practice but, if used, a hypodermic syringe graduated in 1/20th ml and an intra-dermic needle thinner than 6/10th gauge. Site of injection is preferably into the breast muscle (pectoral) and *no deeper than 5 mm*. The pectoral site is painless for the bird.

(ii) *By Mouth:* Use of a dropper or using small pellets (2 mm in diameter and 4–5 mm long).

The latter is preferred, for the exact dose can be given and individual birds can be treated. The former method is hazardous and one never knows how much of the drug the bird has taken.

(b) **Indirect Method**

(i) Via the food—not preferred.

(ii) Via the drinking-water (preferred for smaller birds)

Via the drinking-water is the easiest method, for if the correct dose is added to 1 litre of H_2O the treatment is available for birds of any living mass; a bird drinks according to its mass. Parrots and parakeets drink less H_2O than the smaller birds and the dose is normally doubled. Remember to remove all other sources of H_2O such as fruits, greens etc. and to realize that all birds drink *less* water during cold weather and *more* during hot weather.

CHEMOTHERAPY AND DRUGS (Their Actions and Indications)

For ease of reference the drugs or agents have been grouped into three main categories:

1. Antibiotics, Sulphonamides and Related Agents

2. Antiseptics, Disinfectants, Insecticides and Vermifuges.

3. Nutritional Supplements

1. ANTIBIOTICS, SULPHONAMIDES AND RELATED AGENTS

These substances are termed chemotherapeutic agents which, when introduced into the body, destroy the organisms directly (bacteriocidal action) or render them more vulnerable to the natural defence processes of the body by inhibiting their growth and multiplication (bacteriostatic action).

If the optimum chemotherapy treatment is to be prescribed, it is essential to diagnose correctly, for the indiscriminate use of these 'agents' is not without its dangers.

(a) Sulphonamides
(b) Penicillins
(c) Tetracyclines
(d) Erythromycin
(e) Chloramphenicol (chloromycetin)
(f) Furazolidone and furaldatone ⎫ Not antibiotics but related
(g) Antifungal (anti-mould) ⎭ in their actions

(a) The Sulphonamides

Of this group, Sulphamezathine (Sulphadimidine) is preferred, as it combines low toxicity with effectiveness.

Brand Names	*Indications*
Sulphamezathine (I.C.I., Maybaker, Chevita)	Pneumonias, kidney infections, coccidiosis, E. Coli and Salmonellosis.
Sulphaquinoxaline (Embazin–Maybaker)	Coccidiosis and red mite infestation
Tribrissen Oral Suspension (Wellcome) (= Trimethoprim and Sulphadiazine)	Wide range of infections, safe and highly recommended. Little tendency for bacteria to become resistant.

Dosages are according to manufacturers' instructions and are usually 2 g/litre of water given for 3 days, stopped for 2 days and then given again for a further 3 days, i.e. 3 : 2 : 3 regime. This applies only to Sulphamezathine.

(b) Penicillins

Names	*Indications*
(i) Ampicillin (preferred) (ii) Penbritin (iii) Crystapen	Respiratory tract infections Staphylococcal and Streptococcal infections. Many strains of bacteria are resistant to penicillin.

(c) Tetracyclines

Are divided into 3 groups. All are closely related and are known as broad-spectrum antibiotics.

(i) Chlortetracycline (Aureomycin) 0,25 g/litre H_2O
(ii) Oxytetracycline (Terramycin) 0,50 g/litre H_2O (preferred)
(iii) Tetracycline (Achromycin) 0,25 g/litre H_2O

Indications: Psittacosis (Ornithosis)
Respiratory tract infections
Rickettsial infections
Digestive disorders of bacterial origin

(d) **Erythromycin** (Abbott)

Bacteriostatic action. Not often used as bacteria build up resistance to it.
Indications as for penicillins
Available as Mycosan–t (Chevita)

(e) **Chloramphenicol** (Chloromycetin)

Names	*Indications*
Chloramphenicol (Chevita)	Salmonellosis
	Respiratory tract infections
	Colibacillosis
	Very useful antibiotic

(f) **Furazolidone and Furaldatone**

Widely used alone or in conjunction with an antibiotic.

Names	*Indications*
Furazolidon (Chevita)	Salmonellosis and E. coli
Neftin Premix (Smith Kline)	Salmonellosis and E. coli
Furaldatone (Chevita)	General bacterial infections

(g) **Antifungal**

Names	*Indications*
Nystatin ⎫	Thrush
Mycostatin ⎭	In conjunction with antibiotics

2. ANTISEPTICS, DISINFECTANTS, INSECTICIDES AND VERMIFUGES

Antiseptics–inhibit and stop growth of organisms
Disinfectant–destroys or kills organisms
Insecticides–kill insects.

These agents come in solution, powder, cream and ointment forms and are
mainly used for external application. Here are some non-toxic agents:

(i) Dietreen-T	General disinfectant and insecticide manufactured by Chevita.
(ii) Karbadust® (Carbaryl) powder	Lice and Mites.
(iii) Lopis Bird Aerosol (Pyrethrins)	Lice and Mites and Vermicide for Gape worm.
(iv) Rekotox-P®, (Pyrethrin) (Cooper)	General insecticide but specific for mites, lice and ants etc. Use as for pyrethrin spray treatment.
(v) Vanodine® (Marpet)	Excellent as a general disinfectant for viruses, bacteria, fungi, and also as an insecticide. Can be used internally or externally.
(vi) Panalog Ointment (Squibb)	General topical antibiotic/antiseptic/anti-fungal.

71

(vii) Nebacetin (An antibiotic spray powder containing neomycin and bacitracin)	For dusting wounds and opened 'Bumble-foot' lesions. Wide antibacterial spectrum. Use sparingly.
(viii) *(a)* Chloromycetin Eye Ointment *(b)* Terramycin Eye Ointment	Antibiotic used for most eye infections and sinusitis—apply 2–4 times daily.
(ix) Nystatin Ointment (Squibb)	Fungicidal ointment for cutaneous mycoses, e.g. candida causing crop mycosis in budgerigars. *Not* effective against Aspergillus species.
(x) Medicinal gentian violet (Antiseptic)	For external use only on burns, chronic ulcers and fungal skin infections.
(xi) Betadine Ointment®	Possibly the best all-purpose antiseptic available. Highly recommended.

Some physical agents such as fire or water-vapour are insecticidal (red mites) and disinfectant. Sunrays and ultra-violet are bacteriocidal.

Remember that disinfection is useful but is effective only on clean surfaces; careful cleaning is more efficient than disinfection without cleaning.

Vermifuges and Vermicides (Anti-Worm Agents)

Vermifuge—expels worms
Vermicide—kills worms

Some Examples	*Indications*
Piperazin- + (Chevita) Antepar Tramisol (preferred) Coopane (Piperazine adipate) Tetramisole	Roundworms (Ascarids and Capillaria)
Dicestal (May Baker) Anthelminticum (Chevita) Droncit (Bayer) Lintex	Tapeworms (Cestodes)

3. NUTRITIONAL SUPPLEMENTS

Let us first clear up some misconceptions and rules about nutritional supplements:

Remember:

(i) Antibiotics do not destroy vitamins.

(ii) C.L.O. contributes only vitamins A and D_3.

(iii) Do not keep vitamin preparations for longer than six months.

(iv) Always keep them and all other medicines in a dry, cool place, away from direct sunlight.

(v) Dosages can be increased during 'stress' periods.

(vi) It is advisable and necessary to add nutritional supplements to the diet, especially synthetic vitamins which should be given at least twice a week under normal conditions.

Names	Dosages
Abidec (Parke-Davis)	2 drops per 50 cc water
Vitastress	1 teaspoon to 1 litre water
Multivitamin EB$_{12}$ (Chevita)	8 g to 5 litres water
Multivitamin + (Chevita)	8 g to 5 litres water
Chevita vital	As per manufacturers' instructions
Liverine—Iodine Nibbles (crushed) } Kitzyme (Lopis) crushed	Vitamins and minerals

CHAPTER 12

Post-Mortem (Autopsy or Necropsy)

When confronted with a dead bird, one should first ask oneself: what result would an autopsy give from a diagnostic point of view? i.e. one would not perform an autopsy on a bird which is found beheaded on the aviary floor! If no satisfactory conclusion can be derived from an autopsy then it is advisable to send the bird to a specialized laboratory for microscopical and bacteriological examination.

If a post-mortem is decided upon, then you should approach the bird with the same meticulous scrutiny you would adopt were the bird alive and you were the prospective buyer! By the same token, to know WHAT to look *for* and what you are looking *at* requires some knowledge of the NORMAL. In other words, you can identify the abnormal only if you know the normal. This is important to note. Refer to Introduction.

Materials needed

Cork mat or board ± 20 cm square
One pair fine-pointed scissors 12 cm long
One pair long-pointed tweezers 10–12 cm long
Bowl of cold water
Waste container (to be incinerated with total carcass and remains after autopsy)
Magnifying glass ×10.
Stout pins or small nails
Two test slides or thin glass
Good light
Last, but not least – your own pair of eyes.

Procedure

As shortly after death as possible the body is picked clean and its condition noted. The feathers should be dampened prior to plucking.

(i) Feathers:
Note condition i.e. are they oily and elastic?, dry and brittle?, are they louse-eaten?

(ii) Skin, muscles and feet:
Are the muscles well filled out? Is there any fat beneath the skin? Check for sores, bruises etc. Are the feet in good condition?

The bird should now be placed on its back with wings and legs extended by affixing them to the board with nails or pins.

The skin is now incised (cut) from vent to throat (Fig. 1) and, with the fingers, stripped sideways from the midline incision to expose the muscle layers. Note the abdominal organs. Are they clearly visible? Do the muscles have any dark red or yellow spots on them?

POST-MORTEM

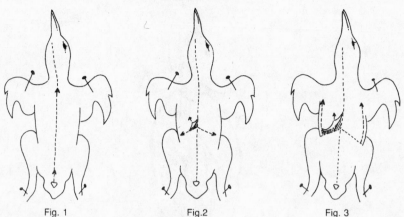

Fig. 1 Fig.2 Fig. 3

A small incision just below and along the margin of the chest cavity should be made with the scissors (Fig. 2). Care should be taken not to damage the underlying organs.

The breast is now removed by cutting through the ribs at each side and raising the breastbone towards the front (Figs. 3 & 4).

Side view

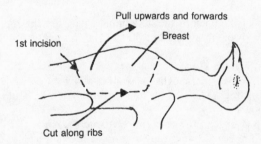

Fig. 4

(Please refer to the anatomy in the various chapters to facilitate identification and to determine position of organs.)

The underlying organs are now exposed and should be identified (Fig. 5). Note that the lungs, kidneys and sex organs are not visible at this stage.

With the tweezers take the gizzard and pull gently upwards, then with the scissors cut above the liver under the heart. This will enable you to remove the digestive system from the abdominal cavity, intact. Be very gentle during this procedure so as not to tear the delicate intestines. Careful 'teasing' of the attached membranes will greatly facilitate the procedure. Place the organs in the container of cold water for further examination later.

75

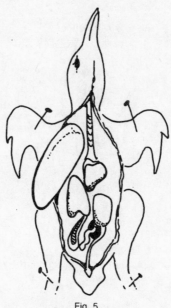

Fig. 5

Inside the chest cavity are the heart and lungs which are normally of a pale pink colour. Below the lungs are the air-sacs (translucid membranes) which are very difficult to see in a small bird unless they are diseased and contain yellow pus-like deposits.

In the centre of the back of the abdominal cavity are the reproductive organs. Testicles clearly visible in a male but the oviduct in the hen is enlarged only when laying.

Further down are the kidneys.

Trachea—to free this, incise with the scissors along the entire length of the neck. The windpipe, or trachea, is a rigid, ringed translucid tube. Cut each end, remove and place in water.

The next step is to strip the skin entirely from the carcass.

The muscles, joints and bones can be examined for any sign of deformity, injury, swelling or discoloration.

Note: The natural colour of tissues, at normal room temperature, will persist for only a few hours after death. Bluish-black, green or other hues develop within 24 hours in the muscles and organs in contact with the gut, liver and especially the gall-bladder (if present), due to bacterial action.

Macroscopic (visible to the naked eye) diagnosis of autopsy findings

Skull:

Presence of haemorrhagic areas (sites of bleeding) in the bony substance of the cranium (skull bone) are a significant finding and will indicate shock, poisoning (chemical or bacterial) or injury etc. (see Chapter 6, Meningeal haemorrhage). IMPORTANT—*The above findings are of significance only if located within an hour of death.* After that period, blood seeps into the bony substance of the skull and is often mistaken for evidence of head injury by the inexperienced examiner; merely rubbing with a finger greatly accentuate this effect.

Meningeal haemorrage

SUMMARY

Organ	Finding/Observation	Diagnosis
Trachea	Presence of little black spots (best seen when placed between two glass slides under strong light and magnifying glass−×10)	Respiratory Acariasis
Liver	Lost colour (pinky, browny, yellowy, pasty white, sometimes lemony yellow) and enlarged	Hepatitis (feeding origin) if subject ill for 2–3 weeks.
Air-sacs	Purulent deposits, sometimes solid Musty white or greenish moulds	Respiratory disease Aspergillosis
Lungs	Fine white-yellow nodules congested and liver-coloured.	Aspergillosis; rarely pseudo-TB. Pneumonia(s)−rare.
Intestines	Congested, vivid pink or red colour Enlarged with liquid inner matter Whitish, creamy inner matter	Enteritis Coli bacillosis Coccidiosis
	Check for worms by adding a few drops of Methylene Blue to the washing and examine in good light. The worms will absorb the stain and be clearly visible.	
Heart	Surrounded by a yellow and sometimes thick tissue	Pericarditis due to infectious disease.
Kidneys	Congested White marks (urate deposits)	Acute nephritis Chronic nephritis

In conclusion, even an autopsy carried out by an expert may not give the exact result.

Specially-equipped laboratories and trained personnel are available for assistance and they should be given as *much* information as possible regarding the ailment etc.

Index

Skin, 39
Sodium chloride, 14
Sour crop, 67
Spleen, 10
Staphylococcal, 51
Streptococcal, 51
Subcutaneous emphysema, 25
Sulphaquinoxaline, 70
Sulphonamides, 69, 70
Sun stroke, 38

T

Tape worms, 48, 54, 56
Terramycin, 70
Tetracyclines, 70
Thrush, 48, 52
Trace elements, 14
Tracheitis, 24
Tremor, 36
Tuberculosis, 51

U

Uraemia, 28
Urates, 11
Uric acid, 11

Urinary tract, 26
Uropygian gland, 45
Uropygitis, 45

V

Vent, 8, 9
Vermicide, 72
Vermifuge, 55, 72
Vessels, 20
Viruses, 48, 50
Virus diseases, 48, 50
Vitamins, 13
  requirements, 13, 73

W

White diarrhoea, 18
Worms
  gape, 54, 55
  round, 54, 55
  tape, 54, 55
Wounds, 67

Y

Yolk retention, 30
Yolk sac, 33
Yolk sac infection, 33